Christmas Carols for Piano

Beginner Christmas Sheet Music Book for Kids and Adults (+ Free Audio)

Christina Levante

Christmas Carols for Piano.
Beginner Christmas Sheet Music Book for Kids and Adults (+ Free Audio)

Christina Levante

2. edition 2023
ISBN: 978-3-9823795-2-4
Sontig Press

Contents

Christ Was Born On Christmas Day

Christmas carol

Bring a Torch, Jeanette, Isabella

Christmas carol of French origin

13
E F♯ G D D C C B A
2 4 1 4 3 2
Christ__ is born, and Ma – ry calls us
C B A G
17
G A B C B A D
1 2 3 4 5
Ah! Ah! Beau – ti – ful is the
B D G F♯

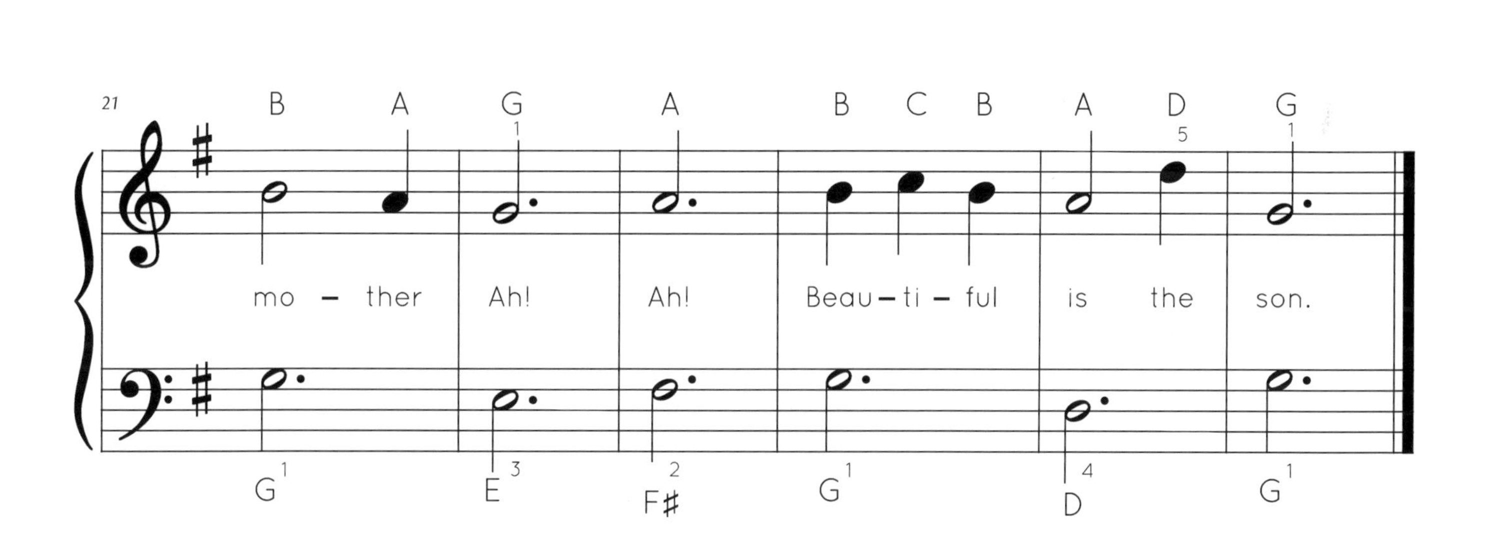
21
B A G A B C B A D G
1 5 1
mo – ther Ah! Ah! Beau – ti – ful is the son.
G E F♯ G D G

Away in a Manger

Christmas carol

9
F F G A F F A B♭
stars in the bright sky look – ed
love Thee, Lord Je – sus, look
all the dear chil – dren in
F F
11
C C D B♭ G A B♭ B♭ C
down where He lay, the lit – tle Lord
down from the sky And stay by my
Thy ten – der care, And fit us for
F G C
14
A A F A G D E F
Je – sus a – sleep on the hay.
cra – dle til mor – ning is nigh.
hea – ven to live with Thee there.
F B♭ C F

Deck the Halls

Christmas carol

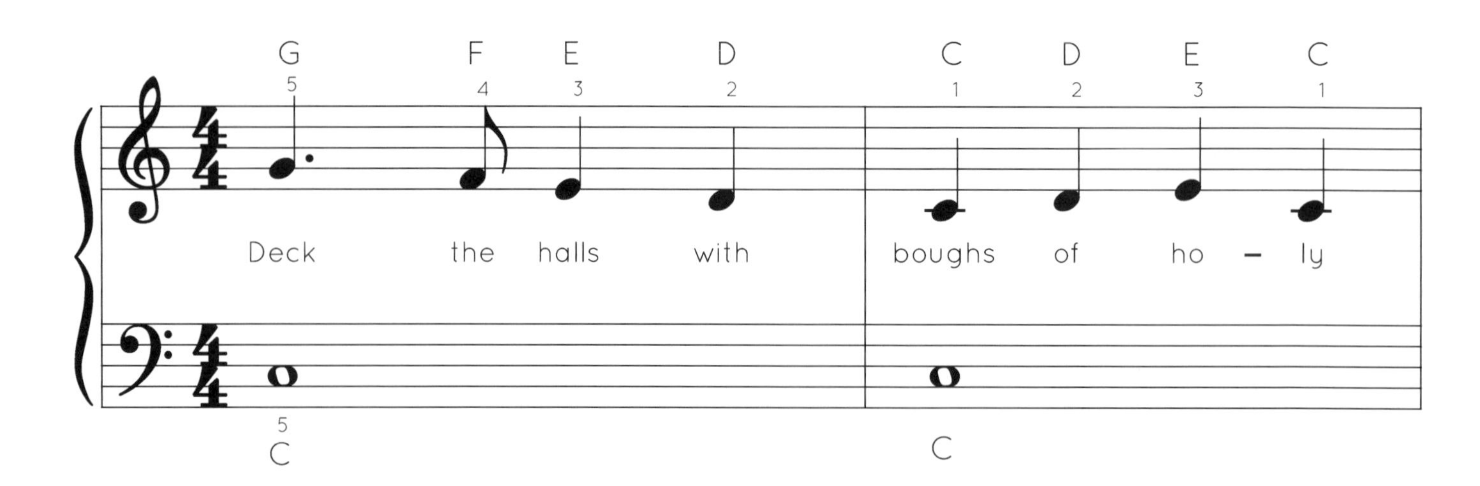

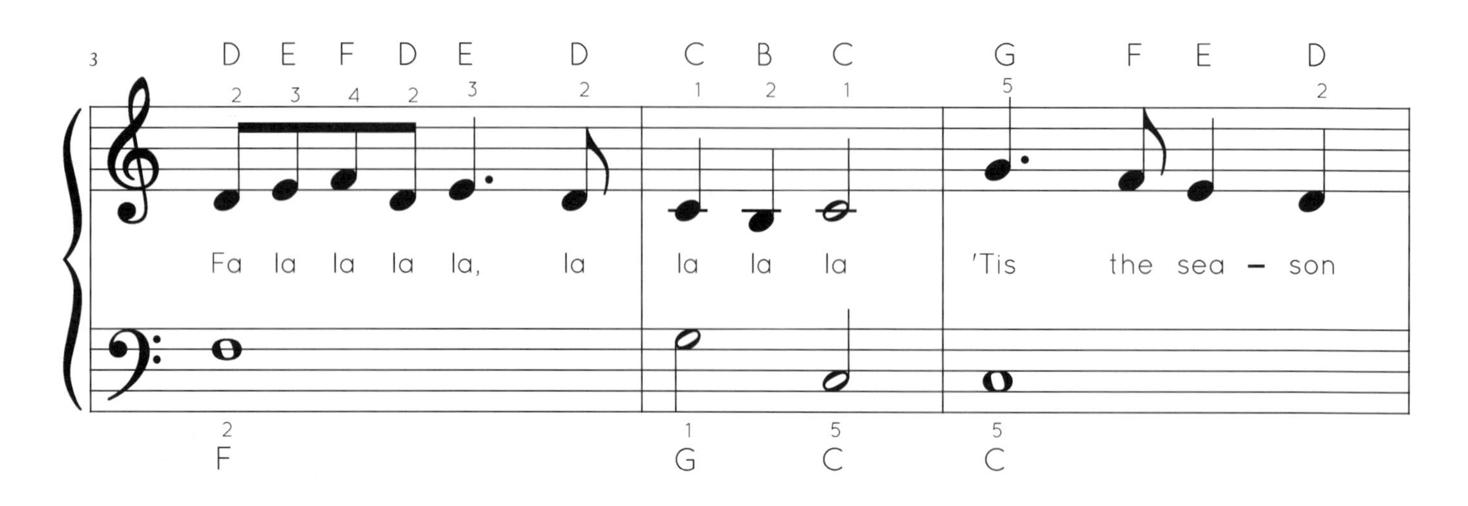

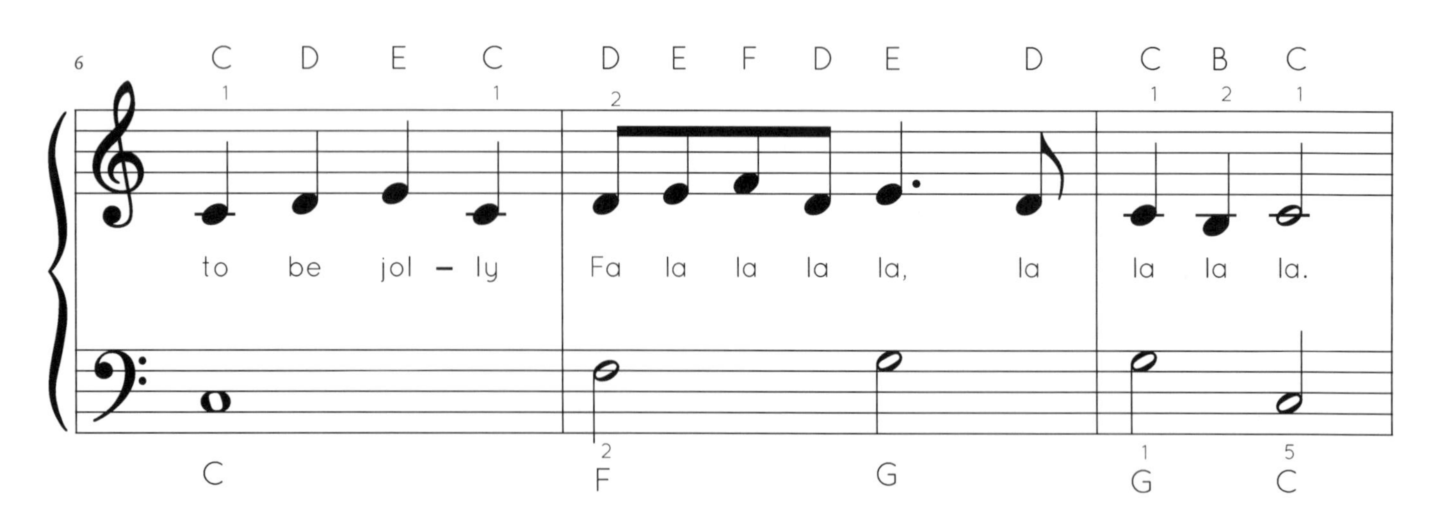

9
D E F D E F G D E F♯ G A B C
2 4 3 5 1 2 3 1 2 4
Don we now our gay ap–pa – rel Fa la la, la la la,
G C C D
12
B A G G F E D C D E C
3 2 1 5 4 3 2 1 2 3 1
la la la. Troll the an – cient yule – tide car – ol,
G C C
15
A A A A G F E D C
5 4 3 2 1 2
Fa la la la la, la la la la
F G C

Joy to the World

Christmas carol

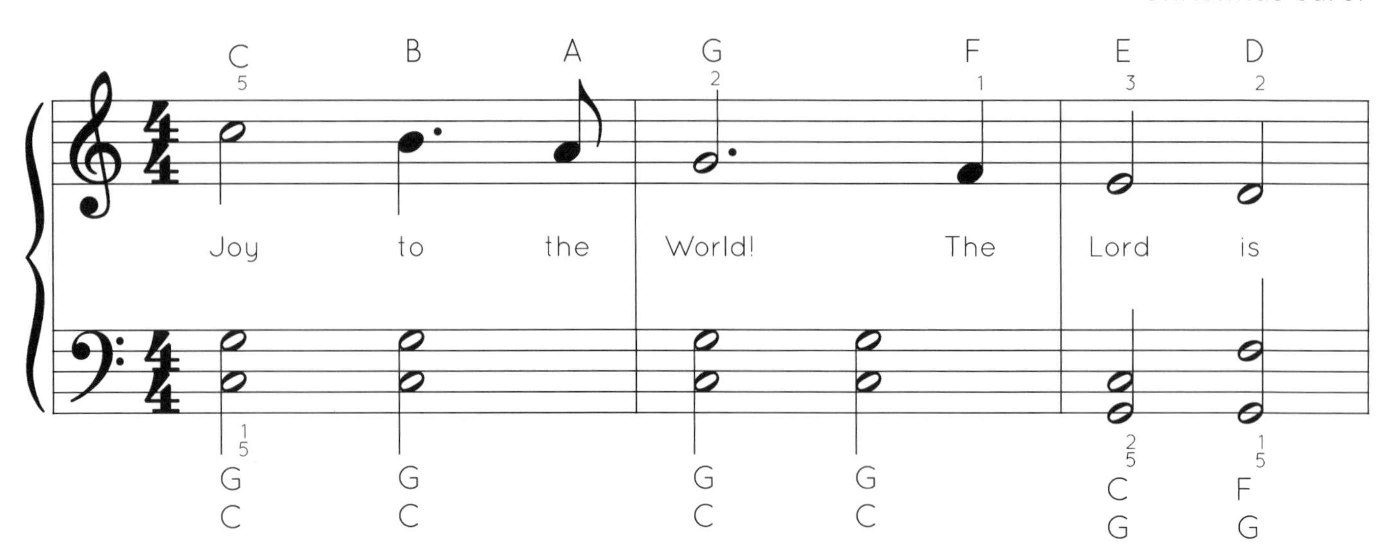

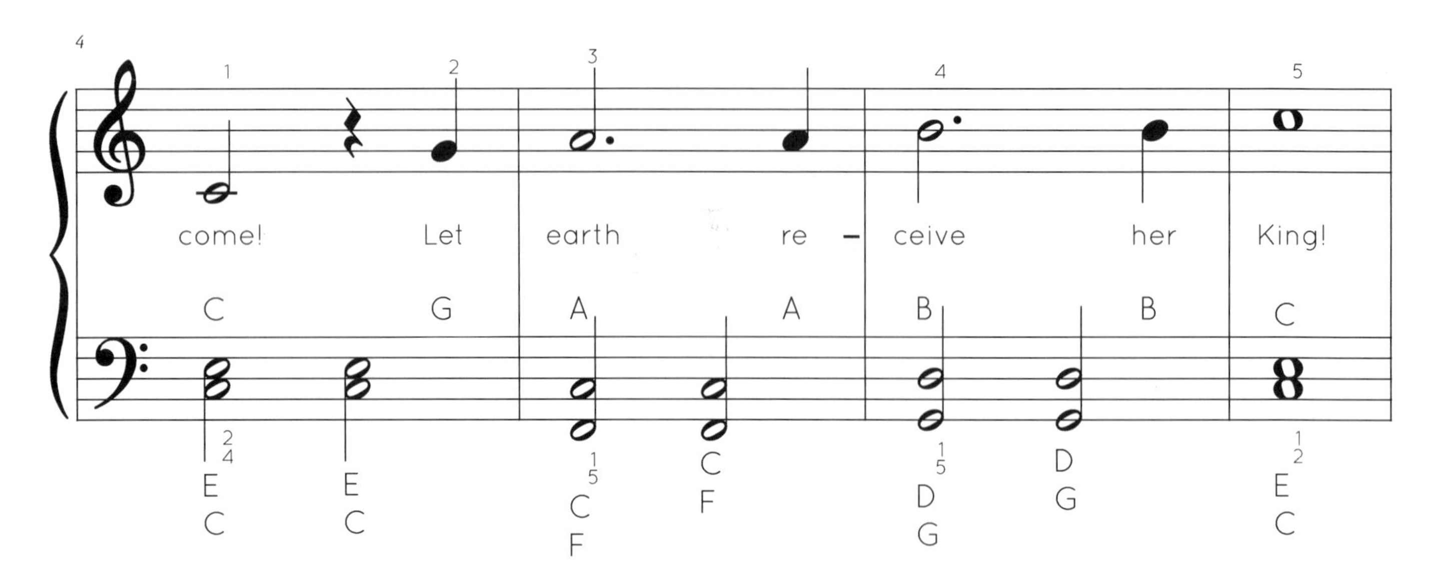

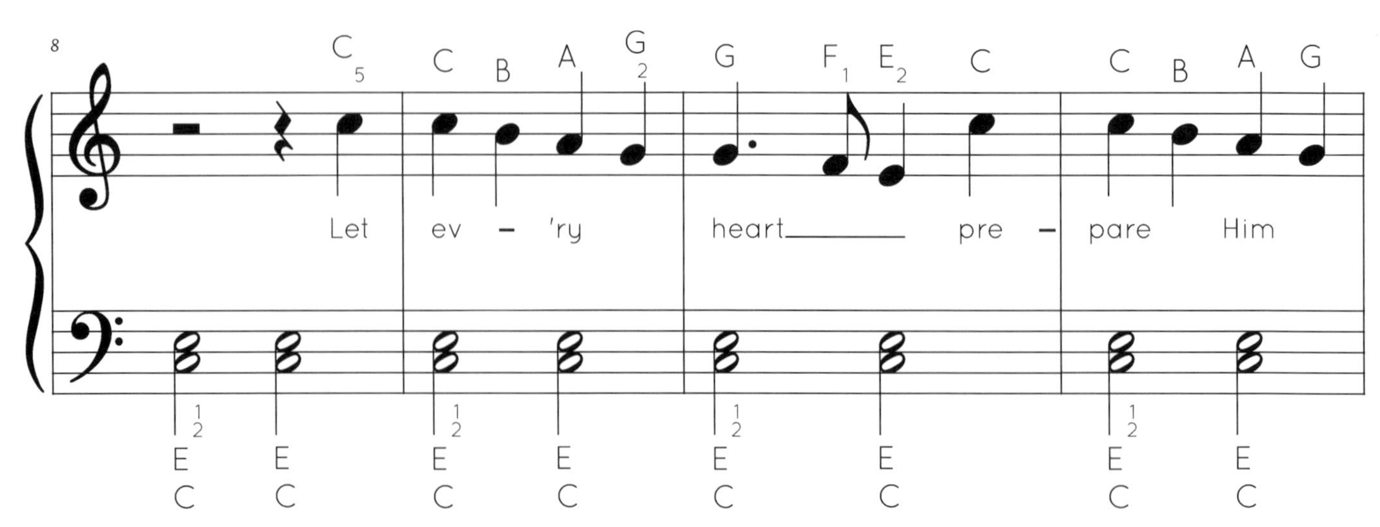

room, And heav'n and na – ture sing; and
heav'n and na – ture sing; And heav'n, and
heav'n and na – ture sing.

O Holy Night

Christmas carol

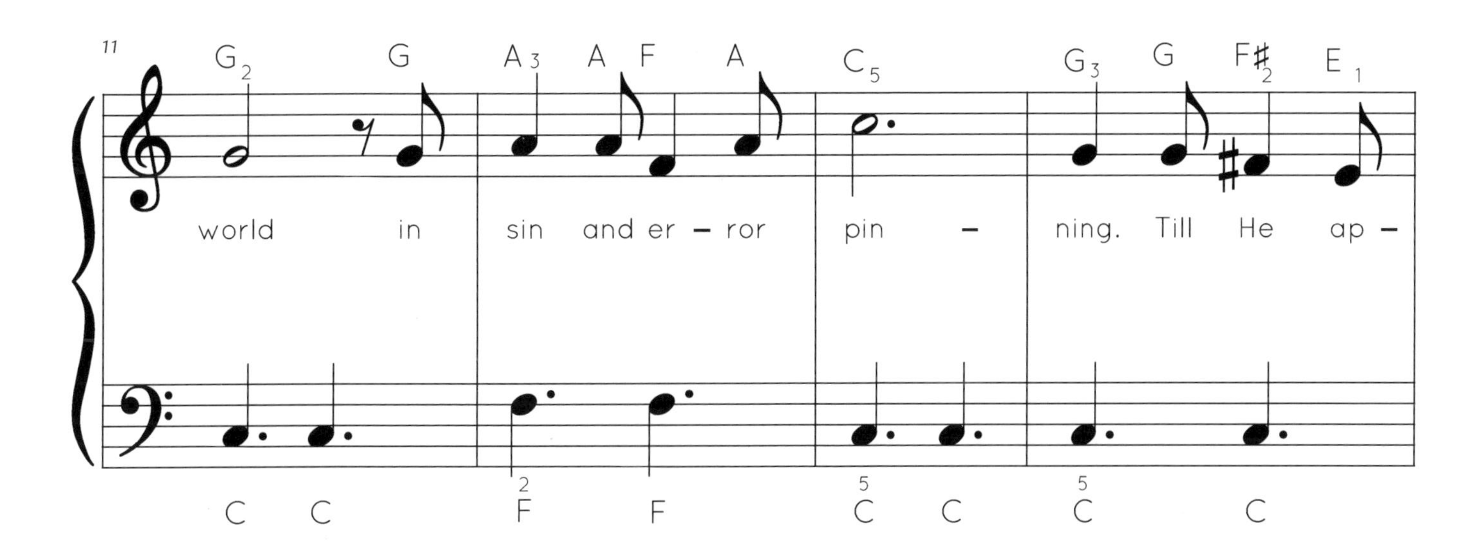
11
G 2 G A 3 A F A C 5 G 3 G F♯ 2 E 1
world in sin and er – ror pin – ning. Till He ap –
C C 2 F F 5 C C 5 C C

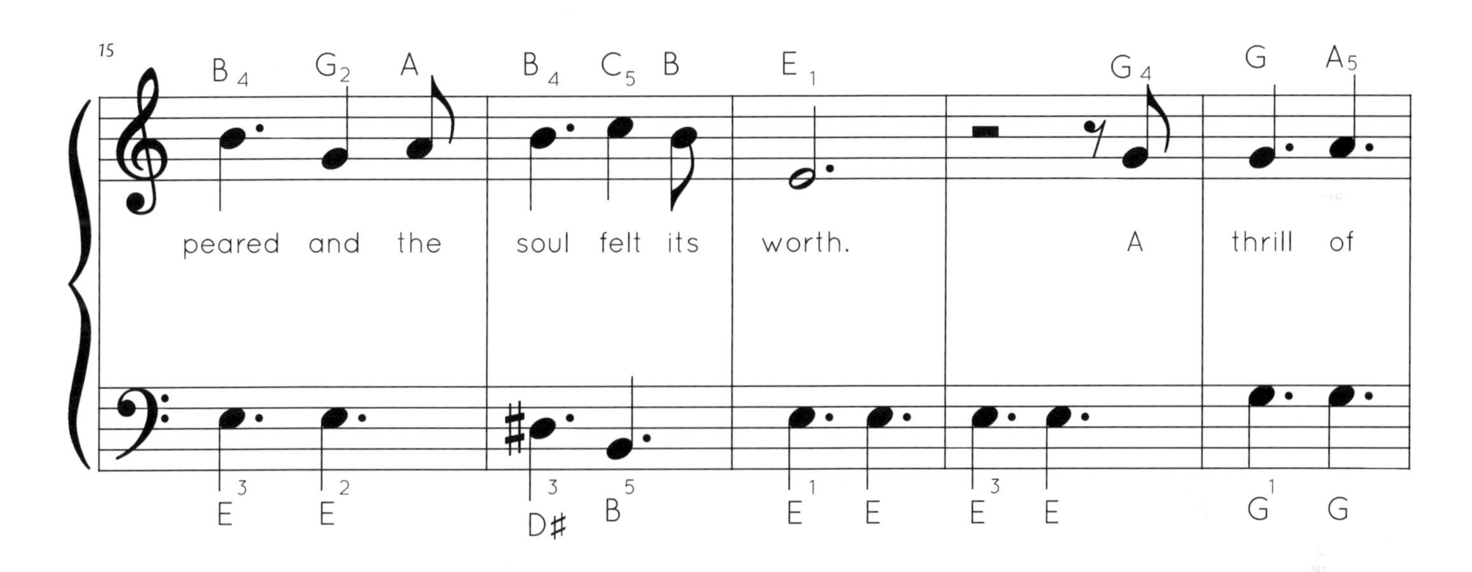
15
B 4 G 2 A B 4 C 5 B E 1 G 4 G A 5
peared and the soul felt its worth. A thrill of
3 E 2 E 3 D♯ 5 B 1 E E 3 E E 1 G G

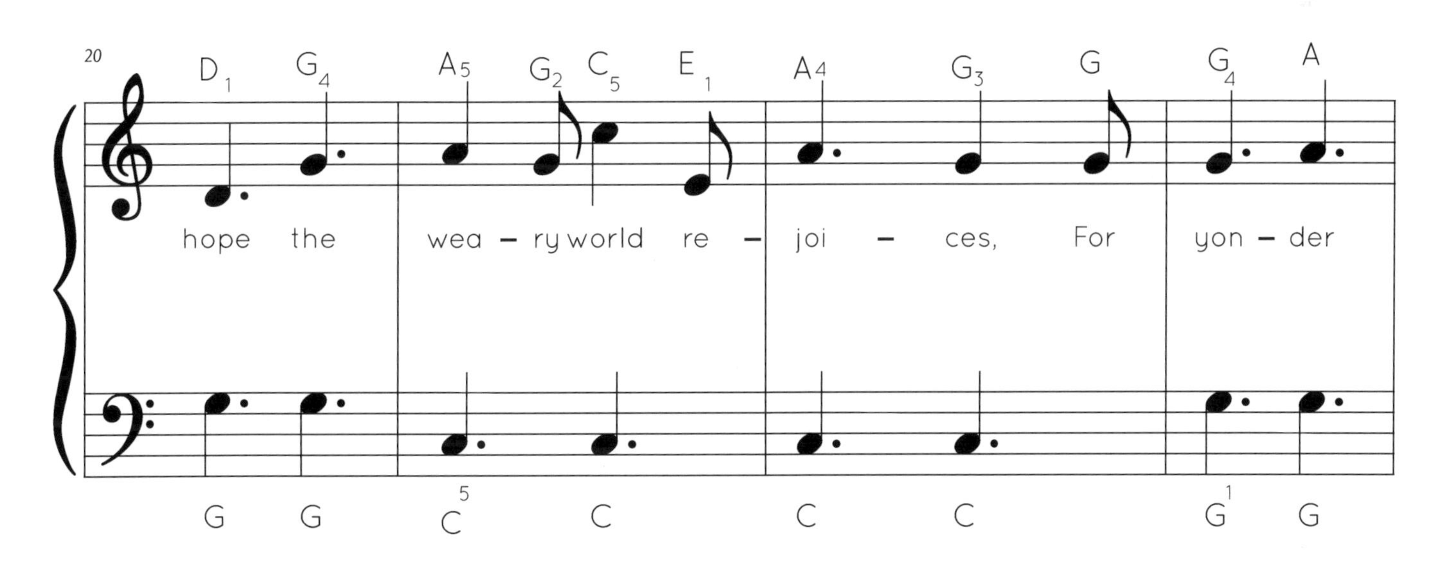
20
D 1 G 4 A 5 G 2 C 5 E 1 A 4 G 3 G G 4 A
hope the wea – ry world re – joi – ces, For yon – der
G G 5 C C C C 1 G G

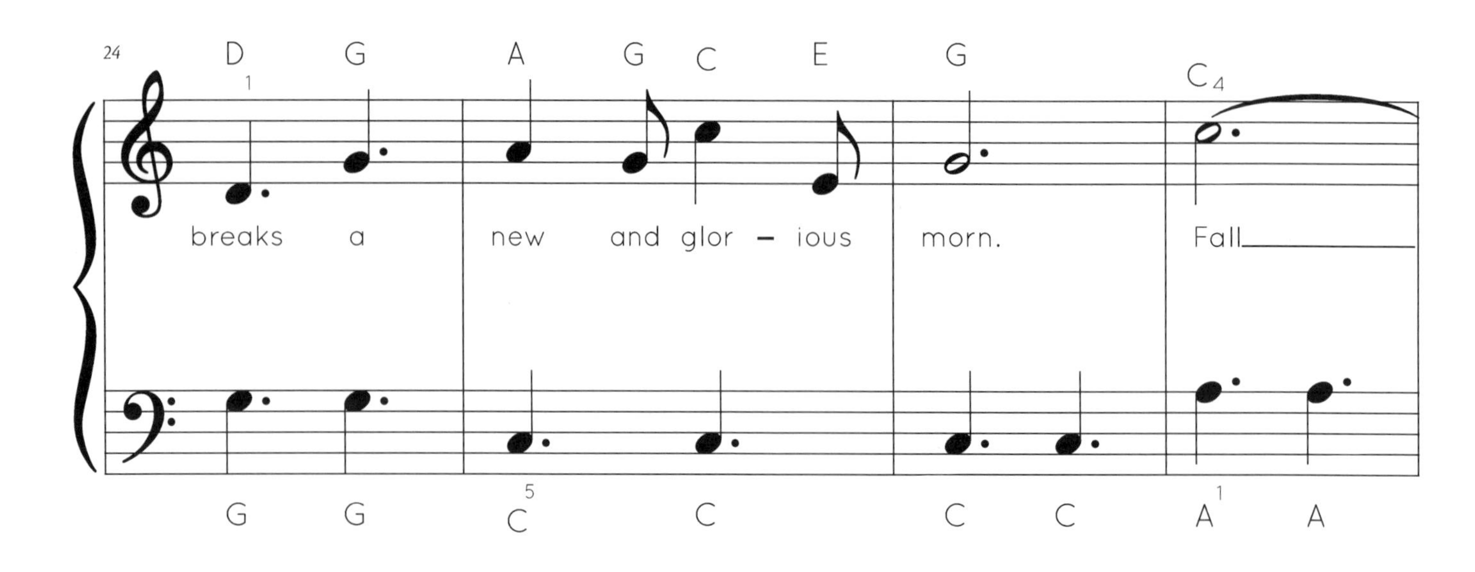
24
D G A G C E G C
breaks a new and glor – ious morn. Fall
G G C C C C A A

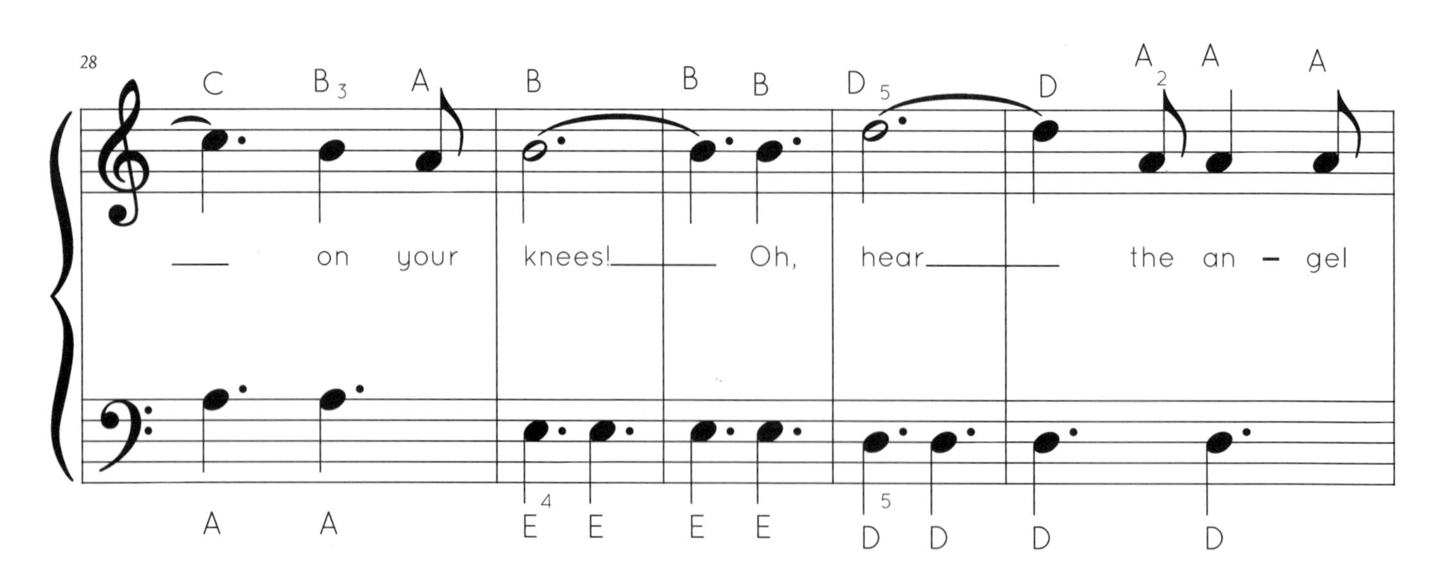
28
C B A B B B D D A A A
on your knees! Oh, hear the an – gel
A A E E E E D D D D

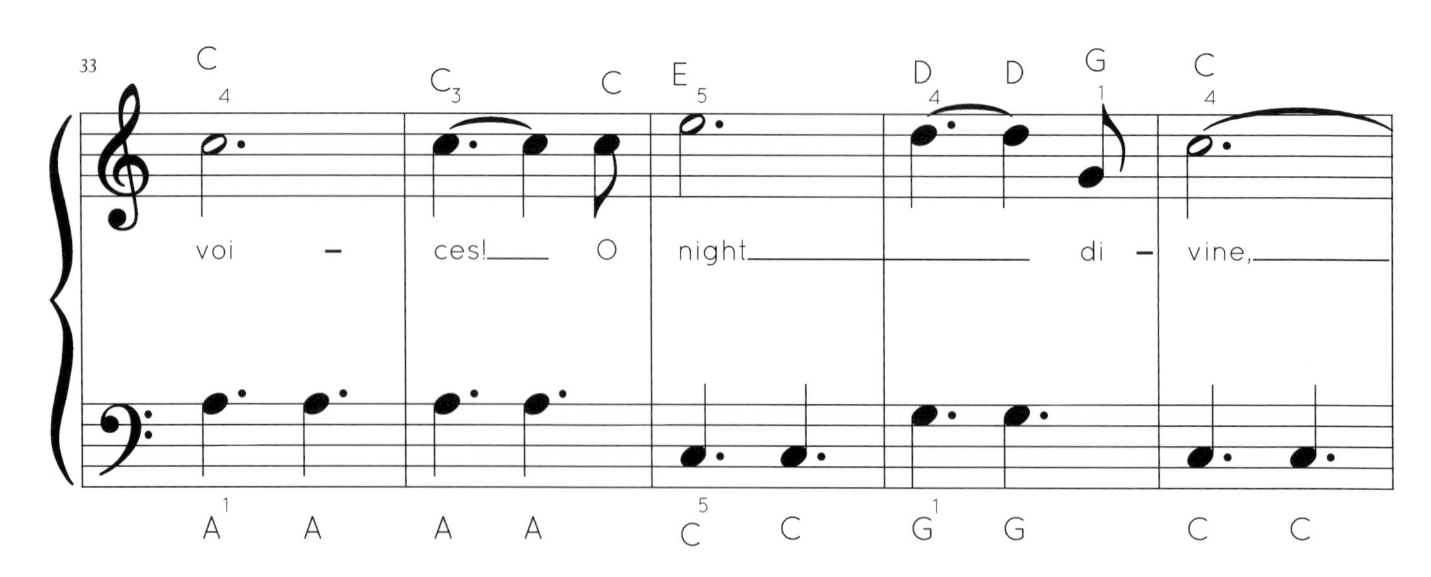
33
C C C E D D G C
voi – ces! O night di – vine,
A A A A C C G G C C

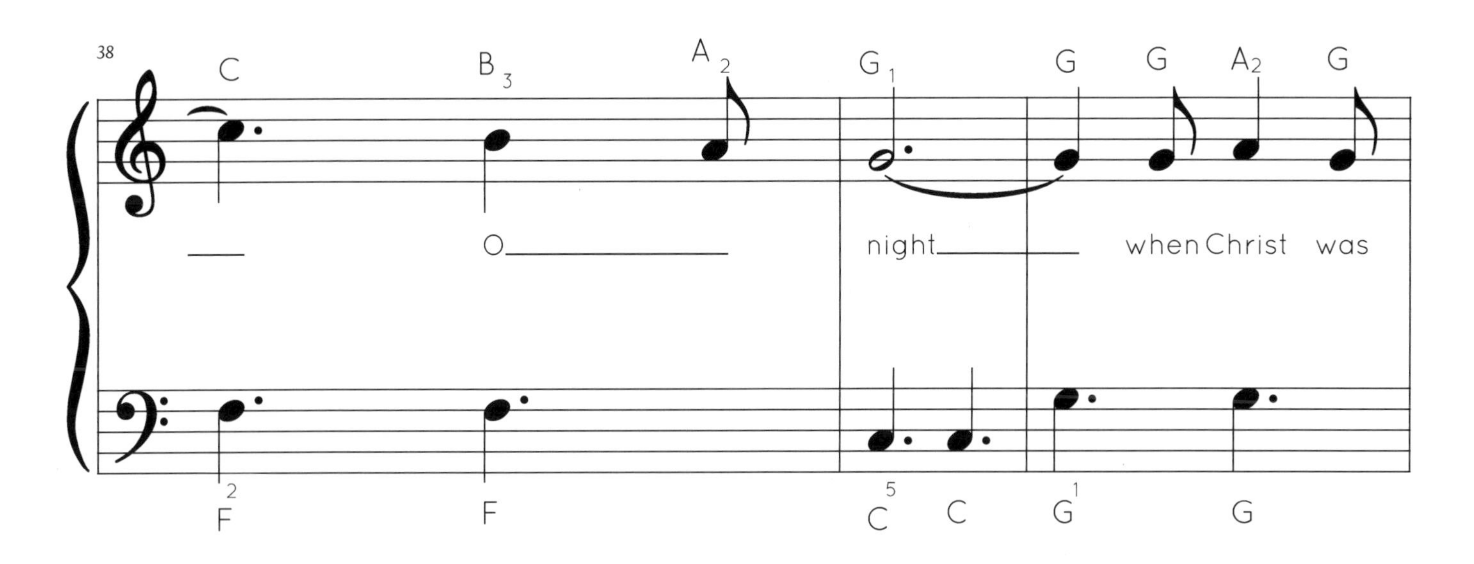
38
C B 3 A 2 G 1 G G A2 G
O night when Christ was
2 5 1
F F C C G G

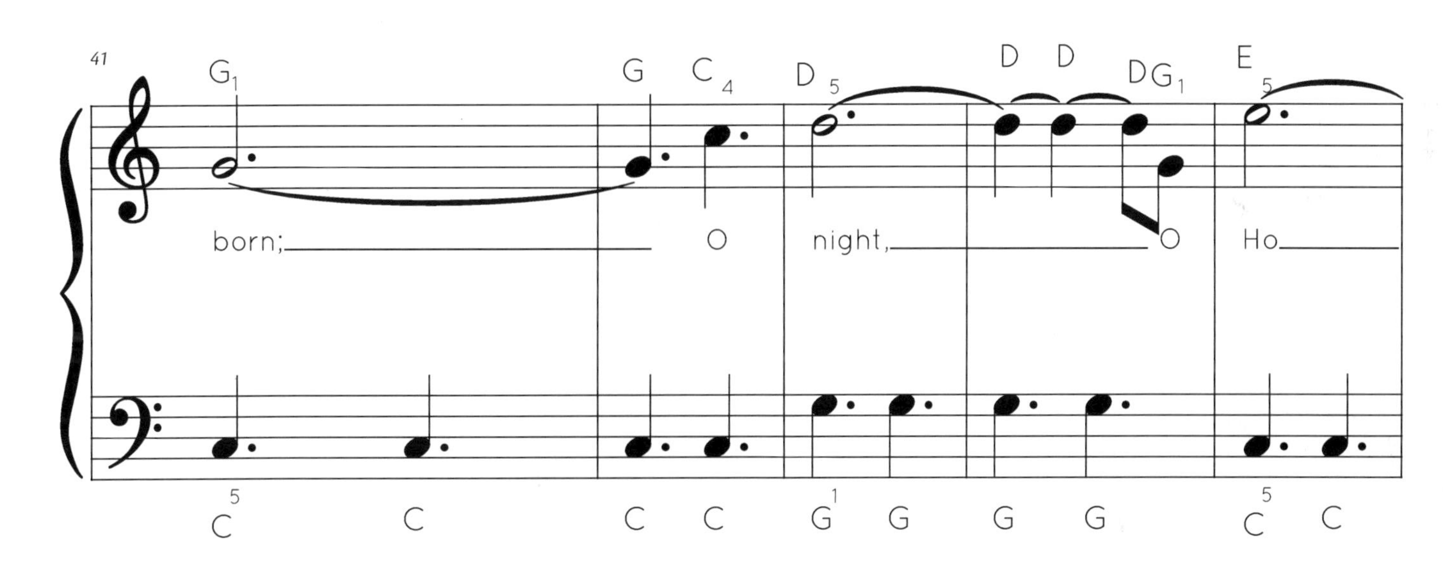
41
G1 G C 4 D 5 D D DG1 E 5
born; O night, O Ho
5 1 5
C C C C G G G G C C

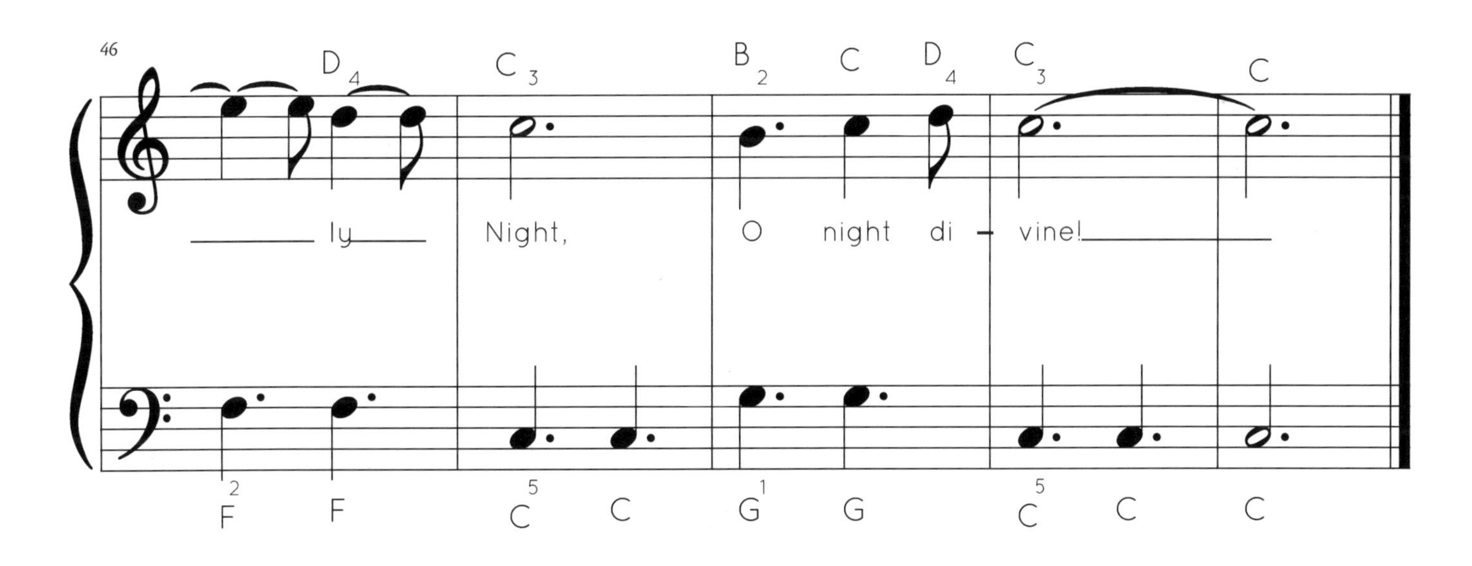
46
D 4 C 3 B 2 C D 4 C 3 C
ly Night, O night di - vine!
2 5 1 5
F F C C G G C C C

Five Mince Pies

Nursery Rhyme

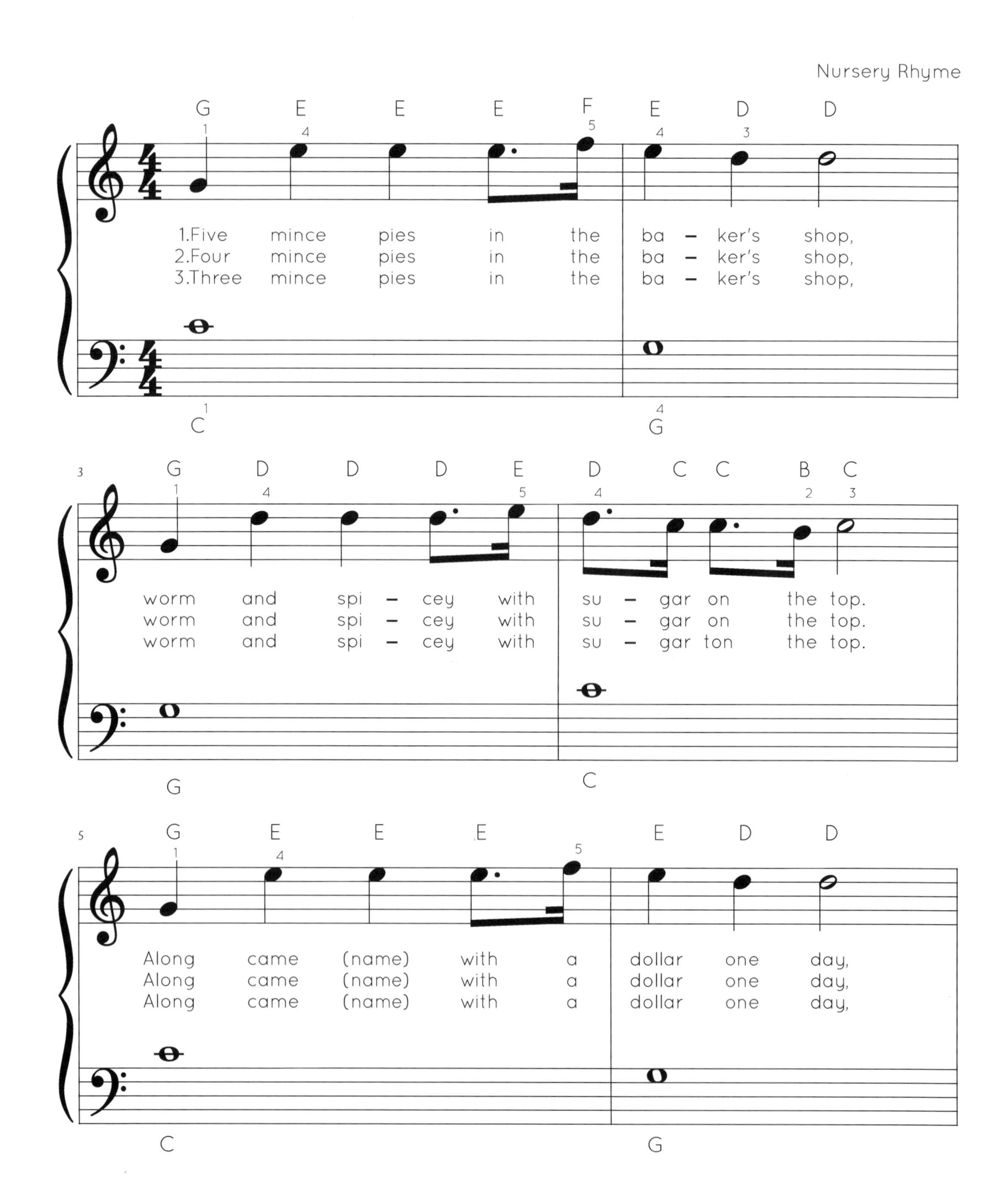

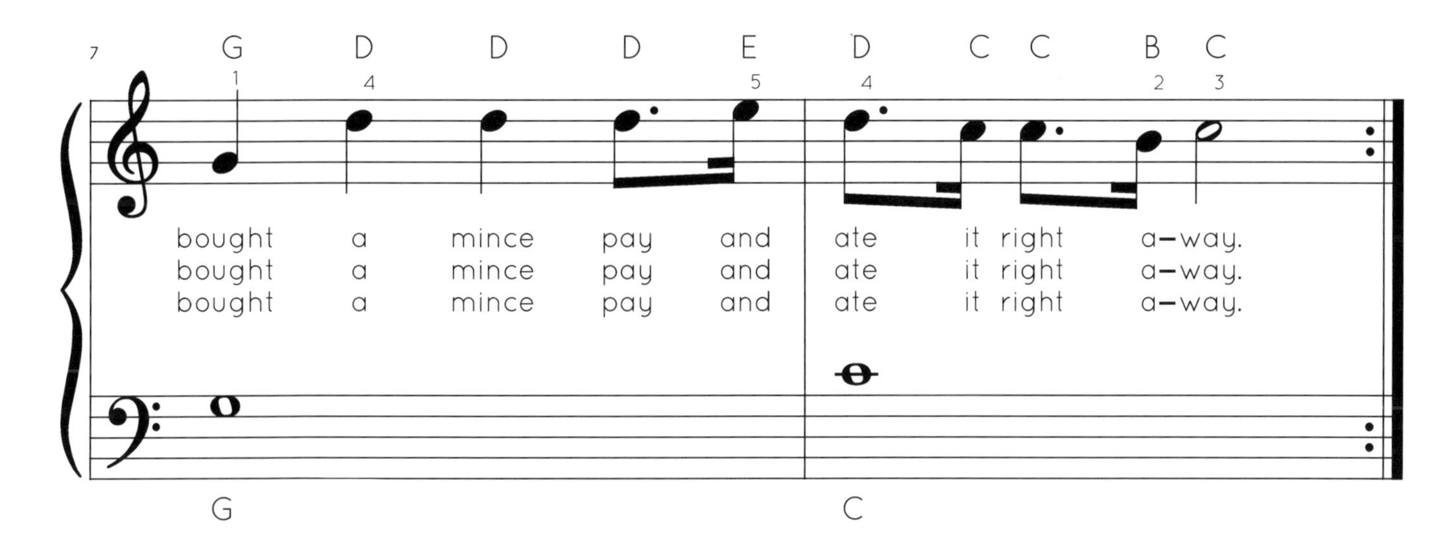
7
G D D D E D C C B C
1 4 5 4 2 3
bought a mince pay and ate it right a–way.
bought a mince pay and ate it right a–way.
bought a mince pay and ate it right a–way.
G C

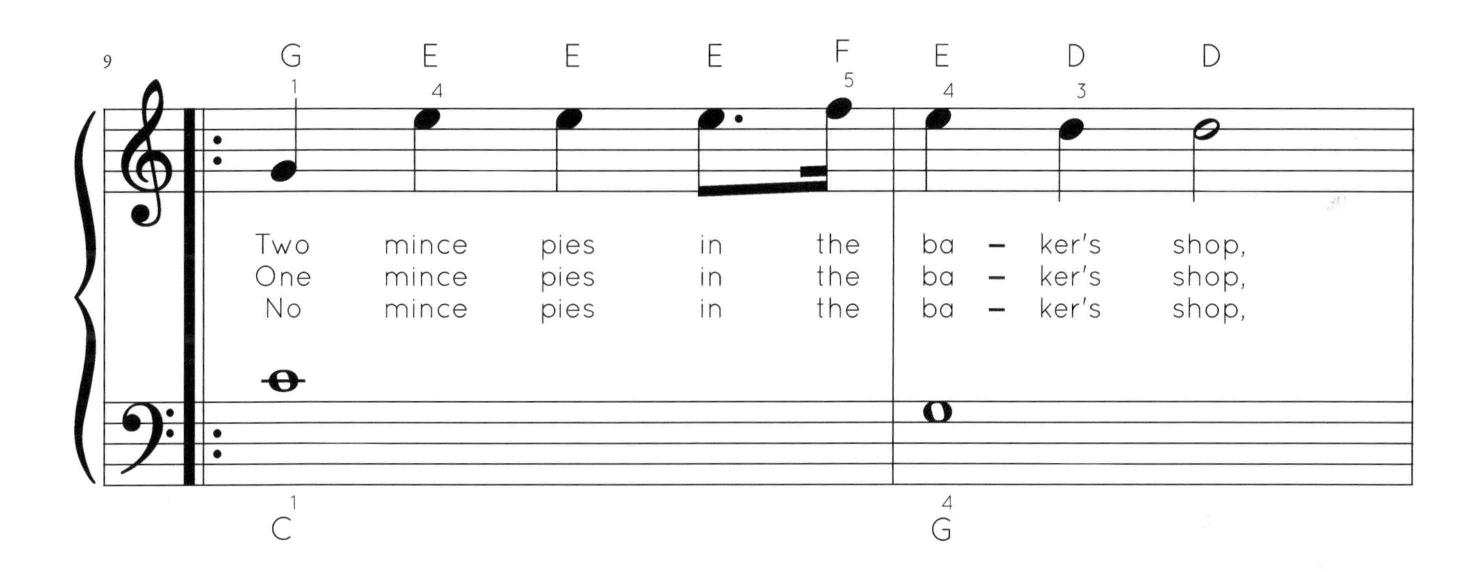
9
G E E E F E D D
1 4 5 4 3
Two mince pies in the ba – ker's shop,
One mince pies in the ba – ker's shop,
No mince pies in the ba – ker's shop,
1 4
C G

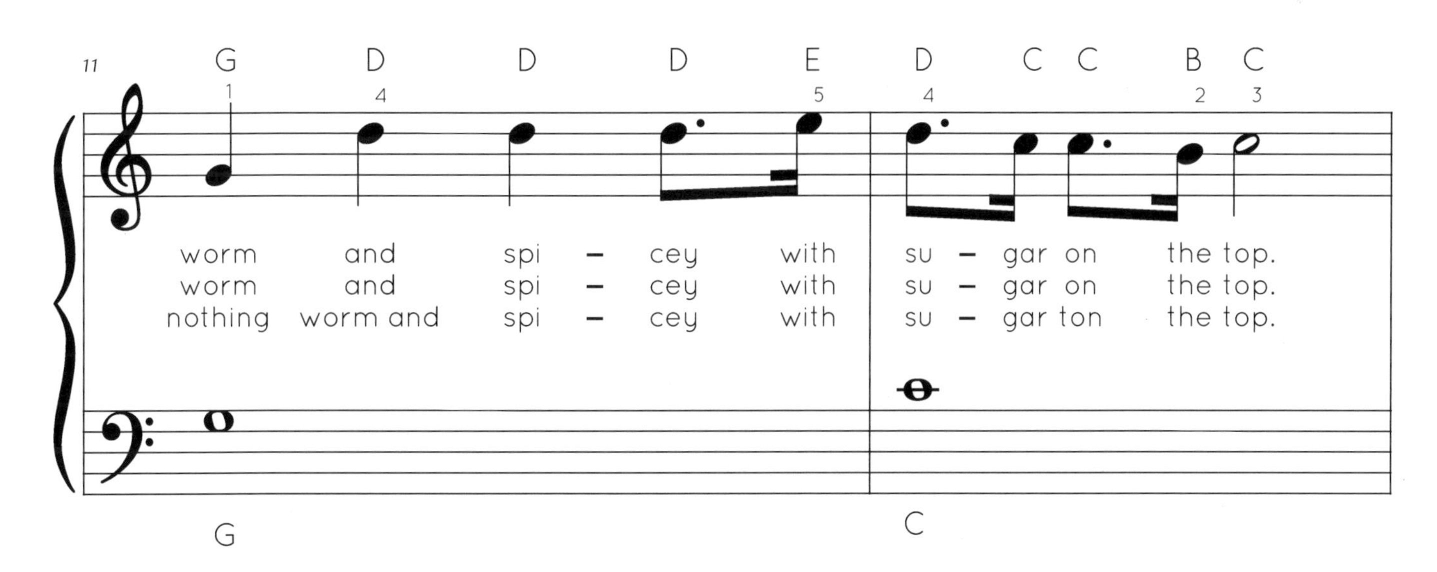
11
G D D D E D C C B C
1 4 5 4 2 3
worm and spi – cey with su – gar on the top.
worm and spi – cey with su – gar on the top.
nothing worm and spi – cey with su – gar ton the top.
G C

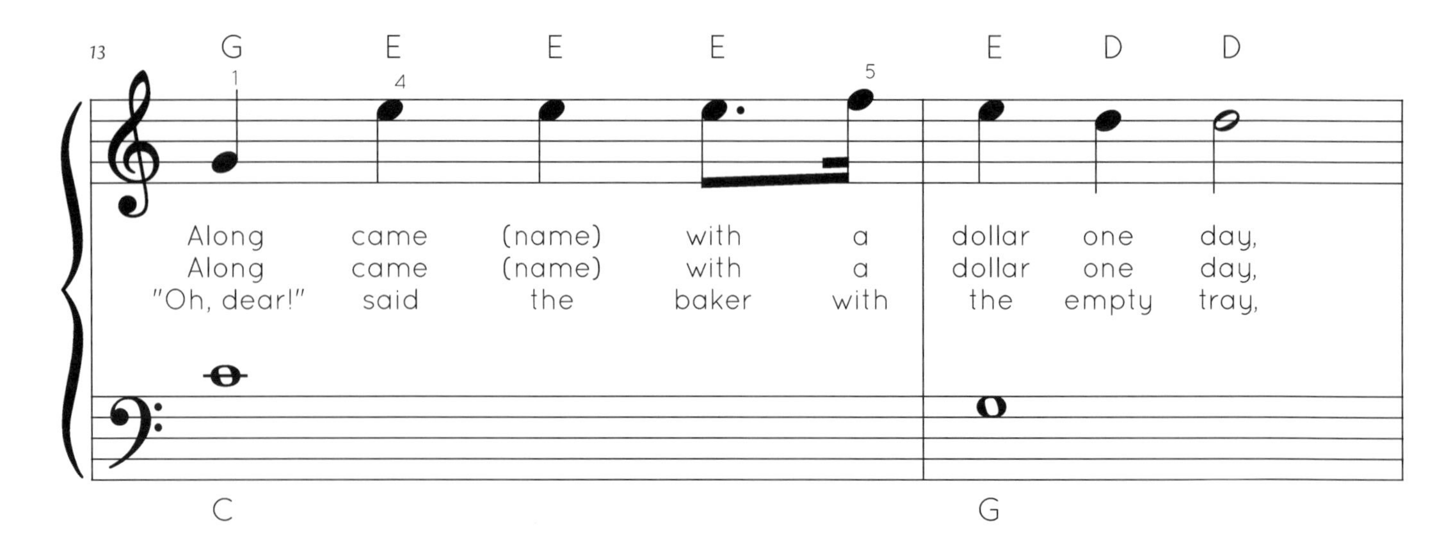
13
G E E E E D D
1 4 5
Along came (name) with a dollar one day,
Along came (name) with a dollar one day,
"Oh, dear!" said the baker with the empty tray,
C G

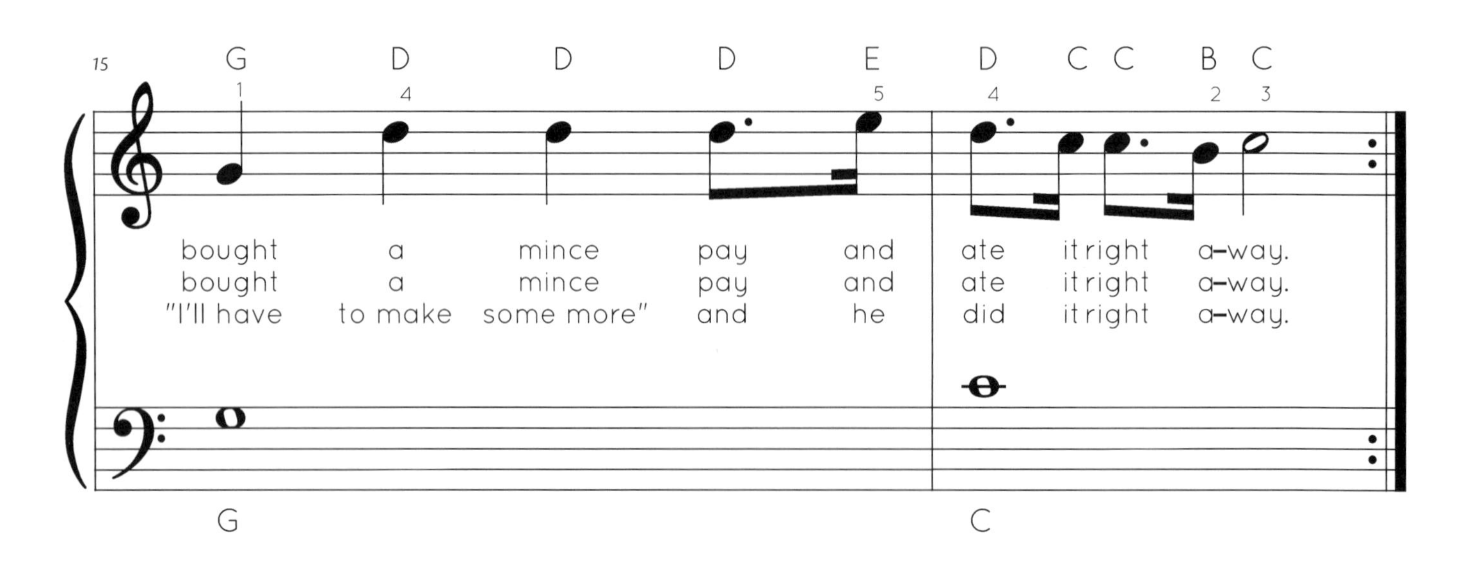
15
G D D D E D C C B C
1 4 5 4 2 3
bought a mince pay and ate it right a–way.
bought a mince pay and ate it right a–way.
"I'll have to make some more" and he did it right a–way.
G C

Los peces en el río

Spanish-language Christmas carol

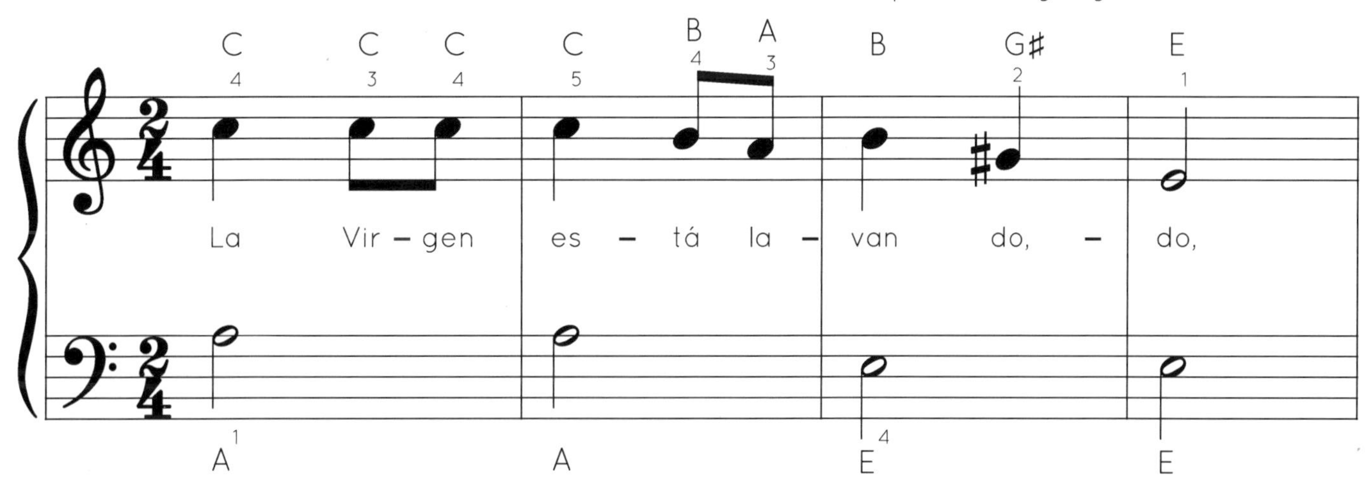

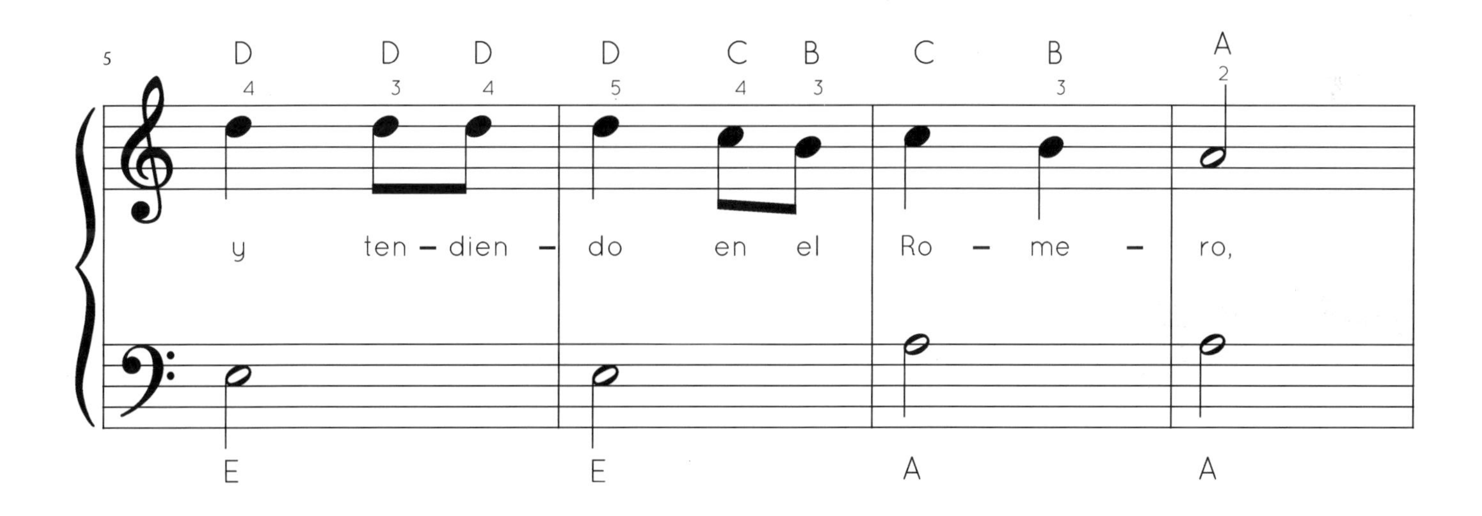

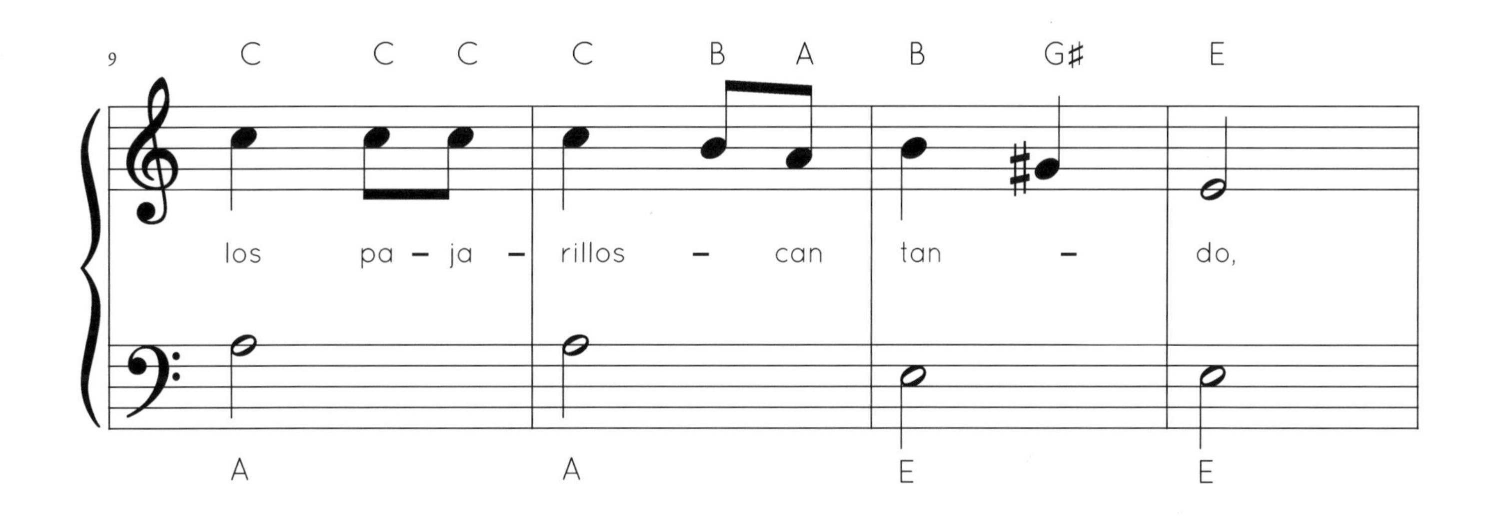

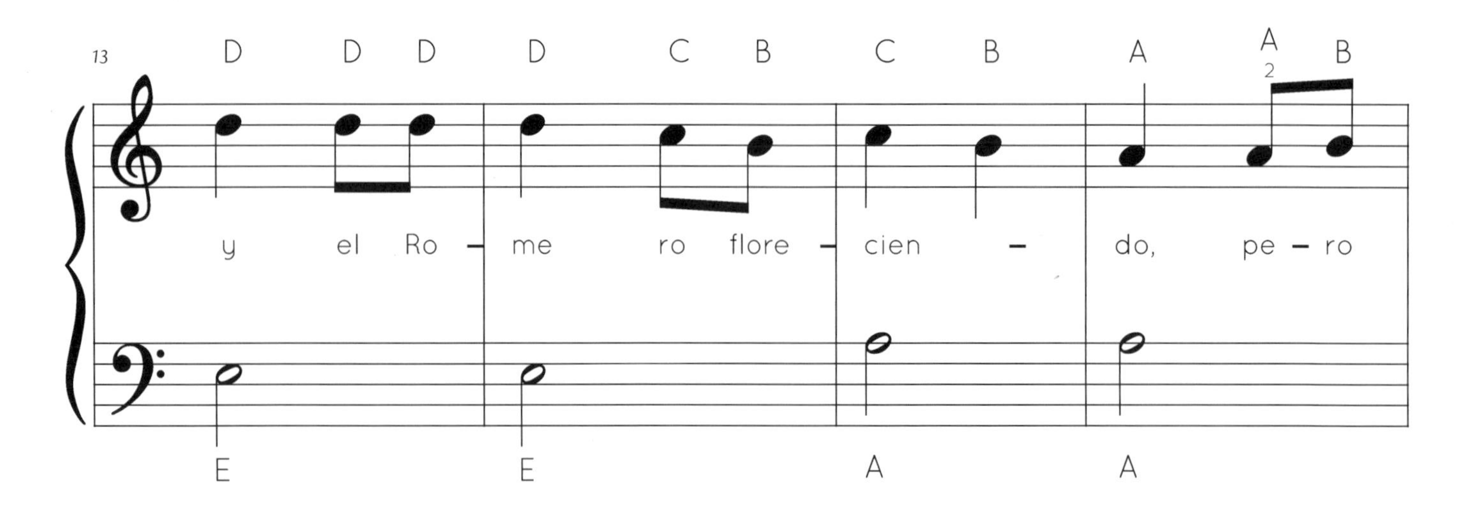
13
D D D D C B C B A A B
2
y el Ro – me ro flore – cien – do, pe – ro
E E A A

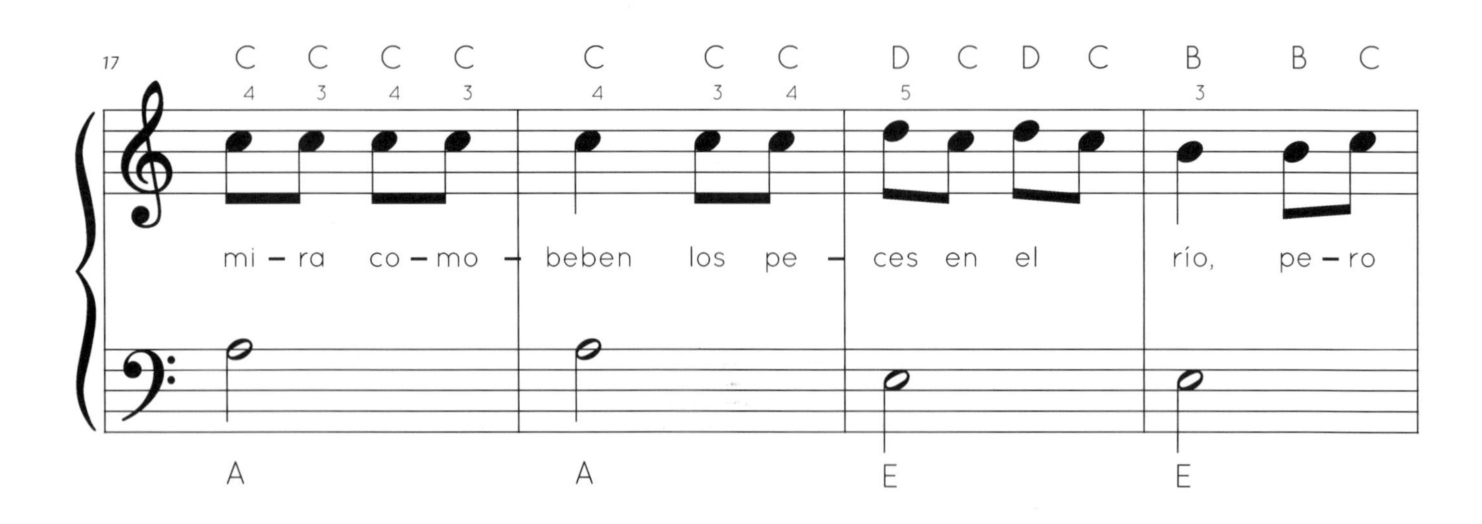
17
C C C C C C C D C D C B B C
4 3 4 3 4 3 4 5 3
mi – ra co – mo – beben los pe – ces en el río, pe – ro
A A E E

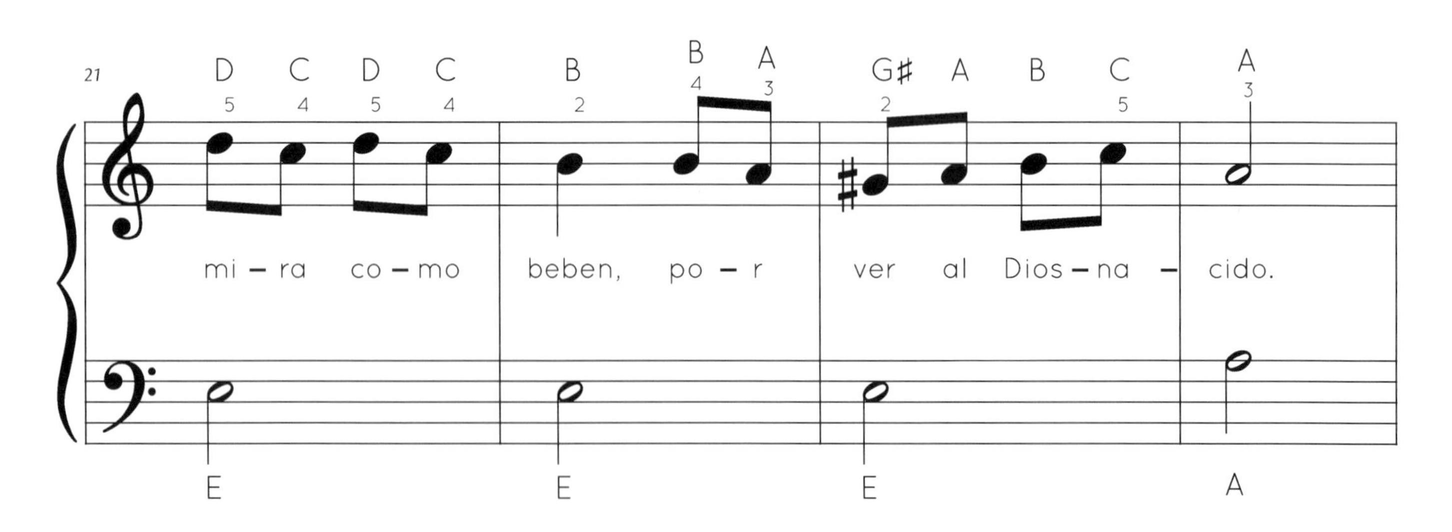
21
D C D C B B A G♯ A B C A
5 4 5 4 2 4 3 2 5 3
mi – ra co – mo beben, po – r ver al Dios – na – cido.
E E E A

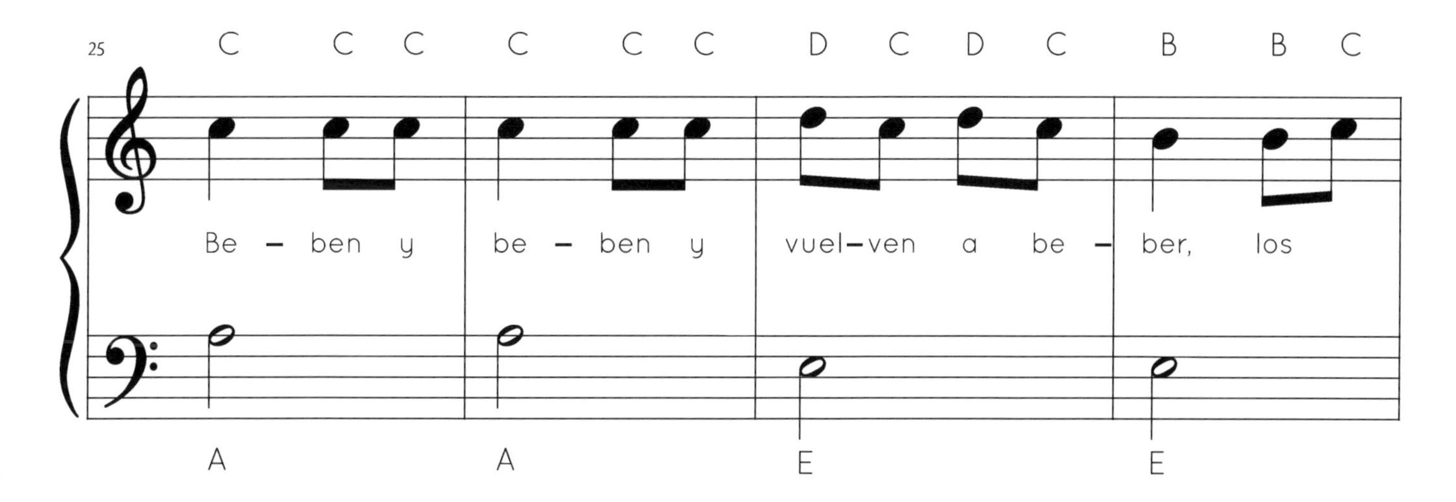
25
C C C C C C D C D C B B C
Be – ben y be – ben y vuel–ven a be – ber, los
A A E E

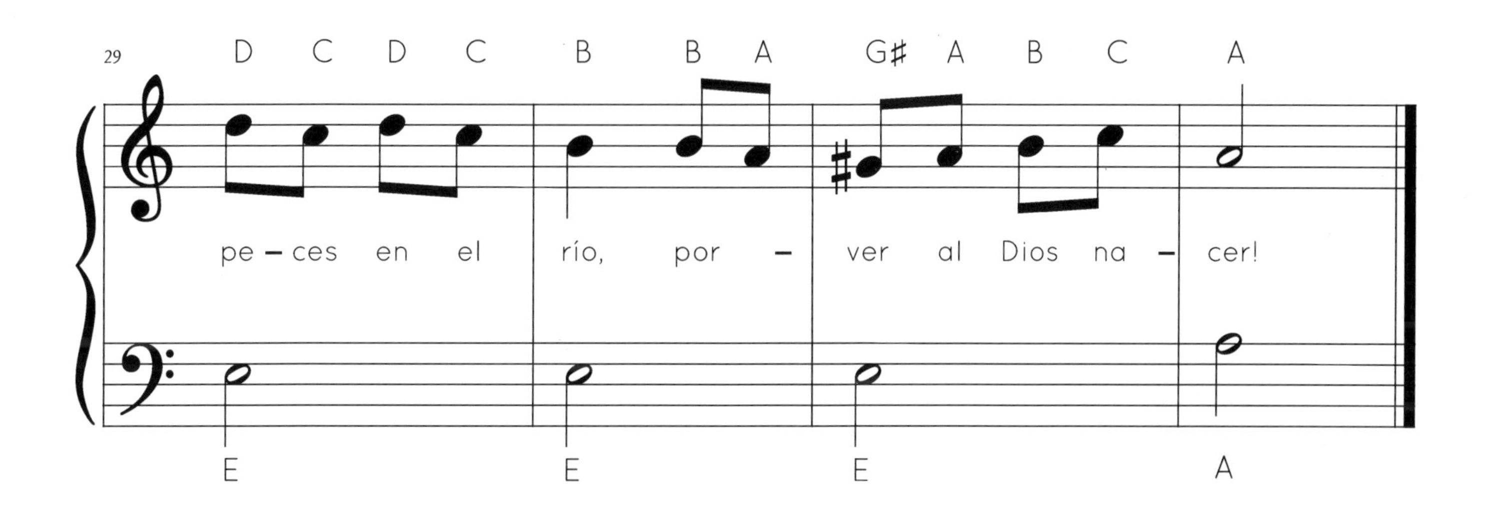
29
D C D C B B A G♯ A B C A
pe – ces en el río, por – ver al Dios na – cer!
E E E A

Once in Royal David's City

Lyrics: Cecil Frances Alexander
Melody: Henry Gauntlett

7
C A A G F E F D D
man – ger for his bed. Ma – ry
cra – dle was a stall: with the
smiles like us he knew: and he
C F
9
C A B♭ B♭ A D D
was that mo – ther mild, Je – sus
poor and meek and lowly lived on
feels for all our sadness, and he
F C F B♭
11
C A A G F E F
Christ her lit – tle child.
earth, our Sav – iour holy.
shares in all our gladness.
F C F

Tu scendi dalle stelle

Italian Christmas carol

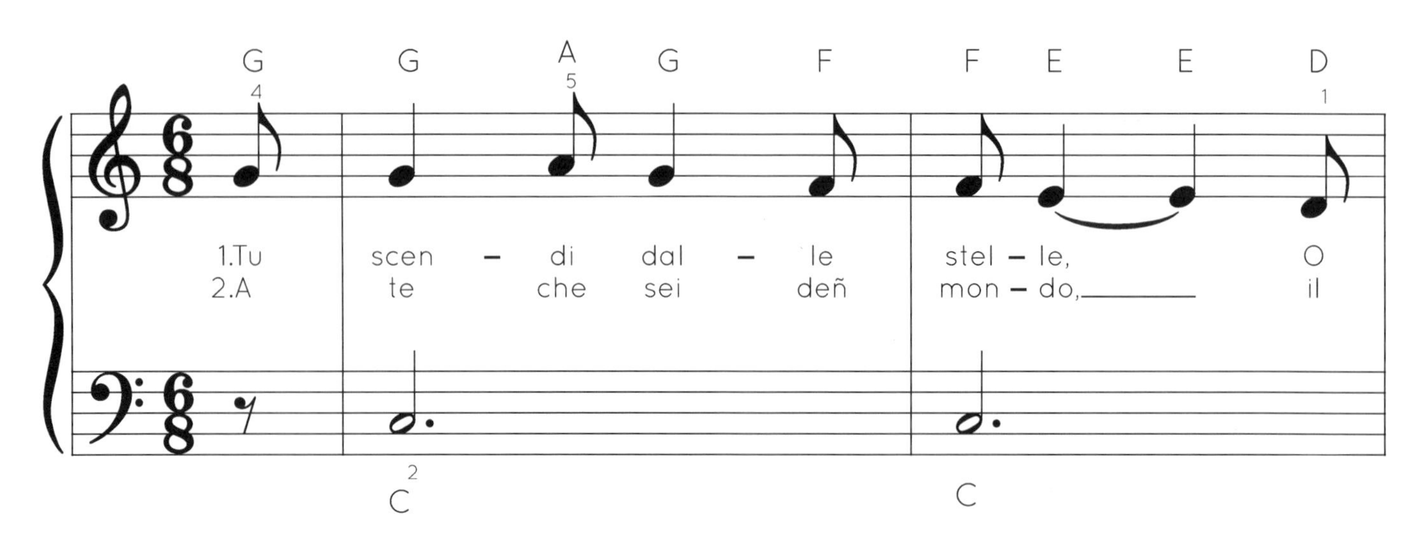

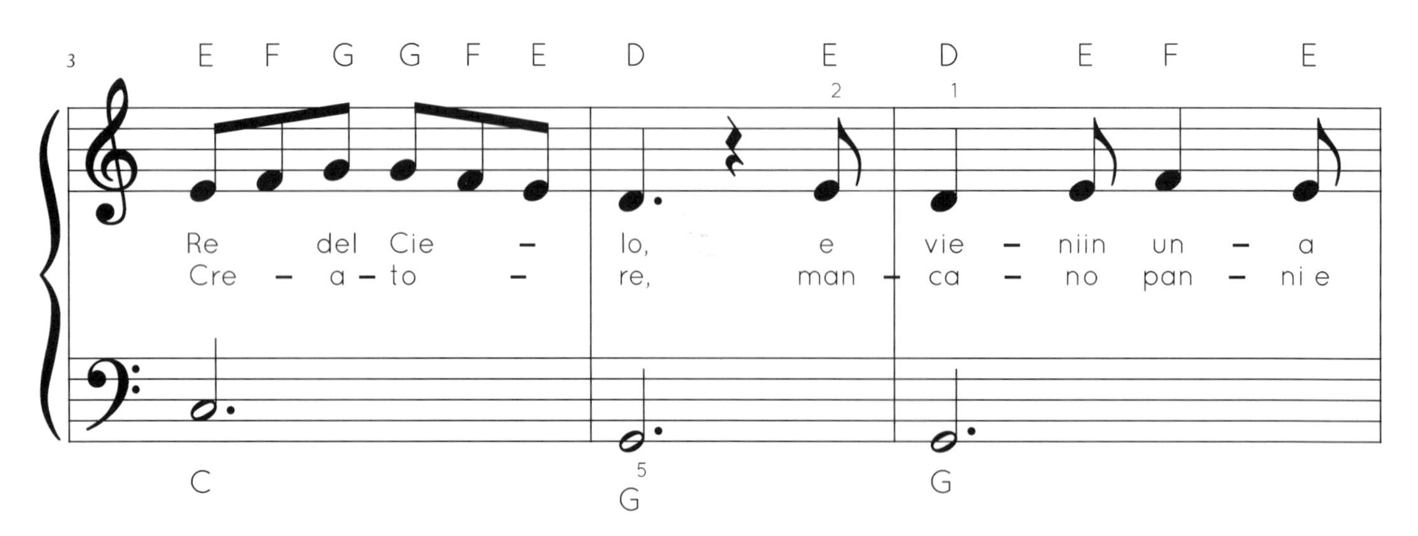

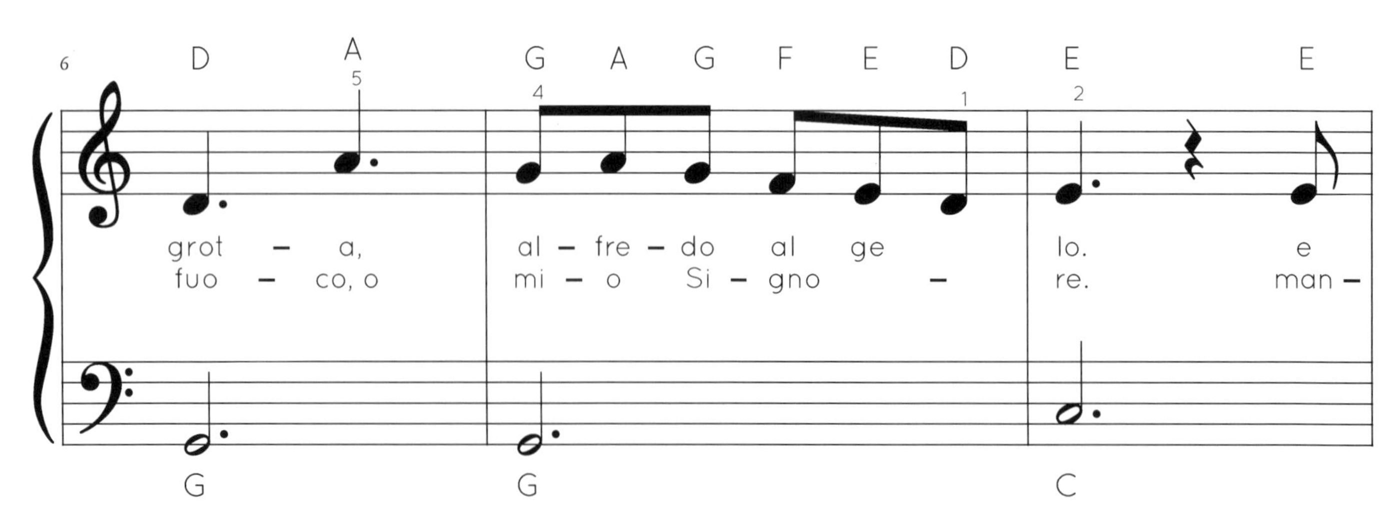

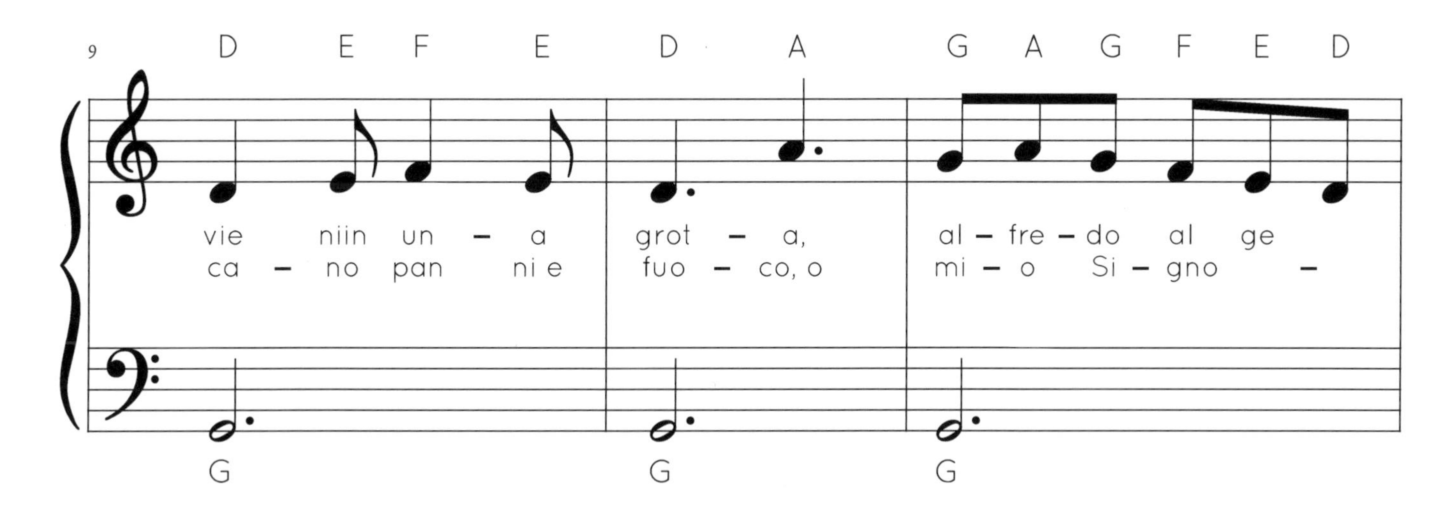
9
D E F E D A G A G F E D
vie niin un – a grot – a, al – fre – do al ge
ca – no pan ni e fuo – co, o mi – o Si – gno –
G G G

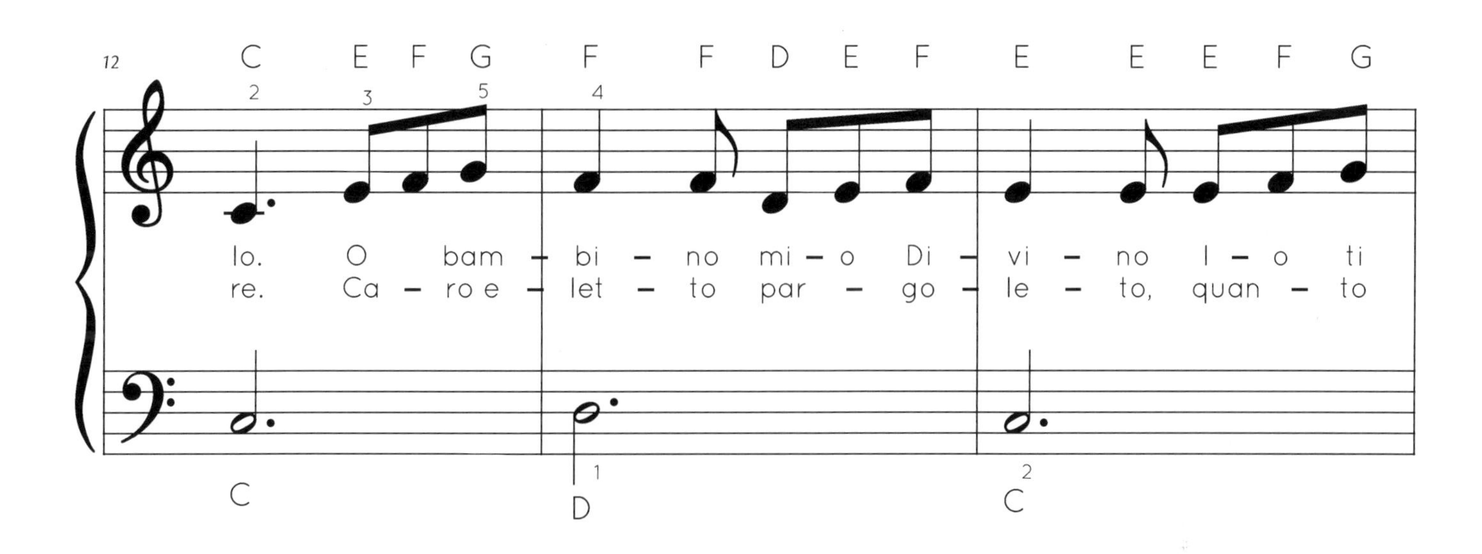
12
C E F G F F D E F E E E F G
2 3 5 4
lo. O bam – bi – no mi – o Di – vi – no I – o ti
re. Ca – ro e – let – to par – go – le – to, quan – to
C D C

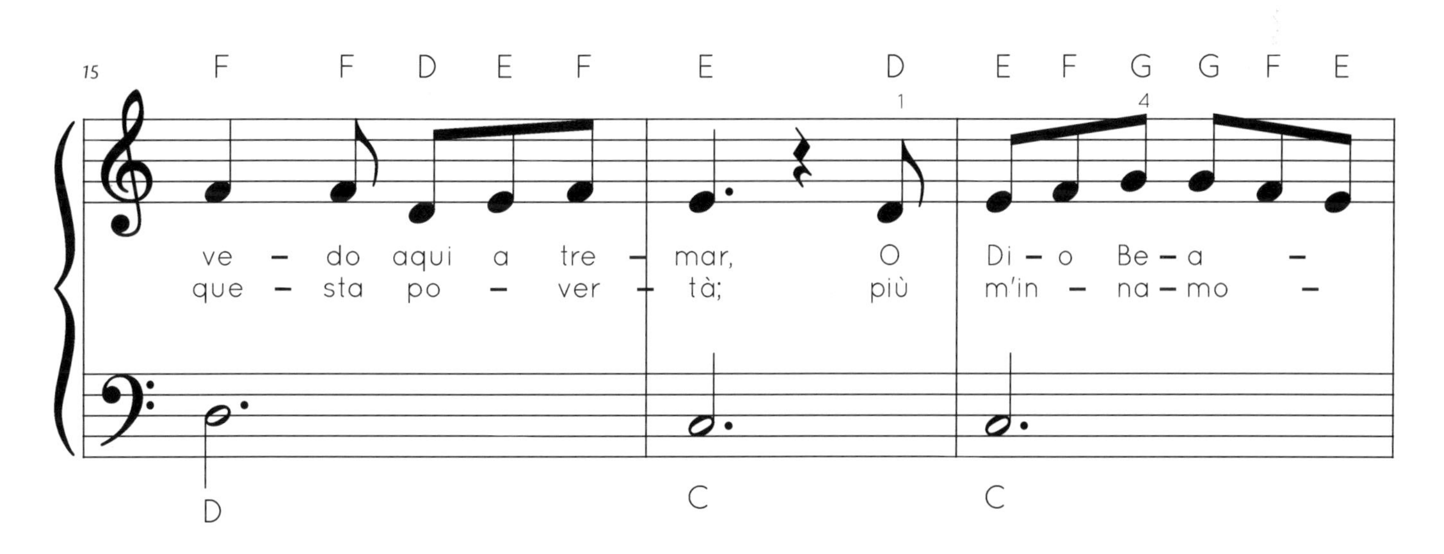
15
F F D E F E D E F G G F E
1 4
ve – do aqui a tre – mar, O Di – o Be – a –
que – sta po – ver – tà; più m'in – na – mo –
D C C

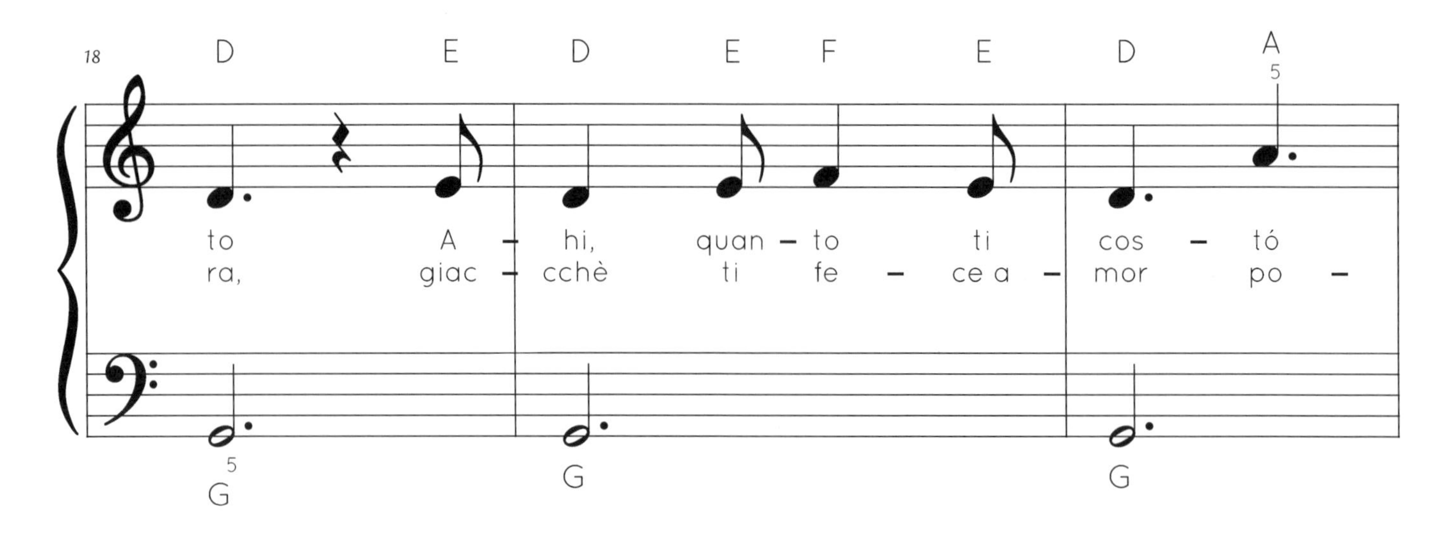
18
D E D E F E D A
5
to A – hi, quan – to ti cos – tó
ra, giac – cchè ti fe – ce a – mor po –
5
G G G

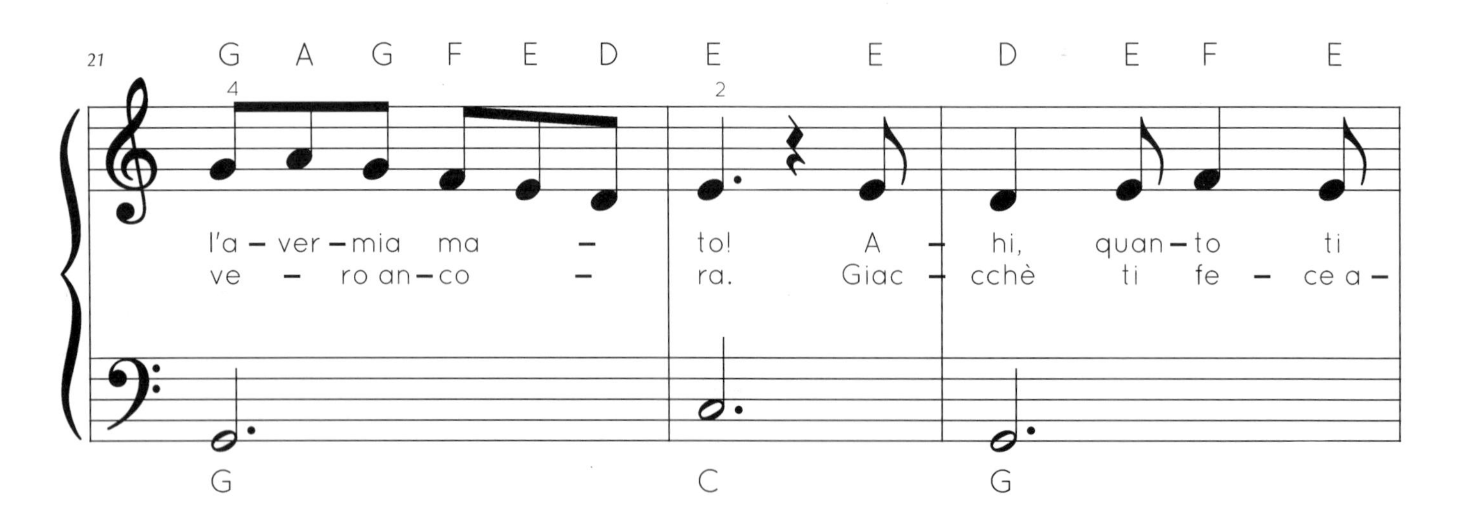
21
G A G F E D E E D E F E
4
2
l'a – ver – mia ma – to! A – hi, quan – to ti
ve – ro an – co – ra. Giac – cchè ti fe – ce a –
G C G

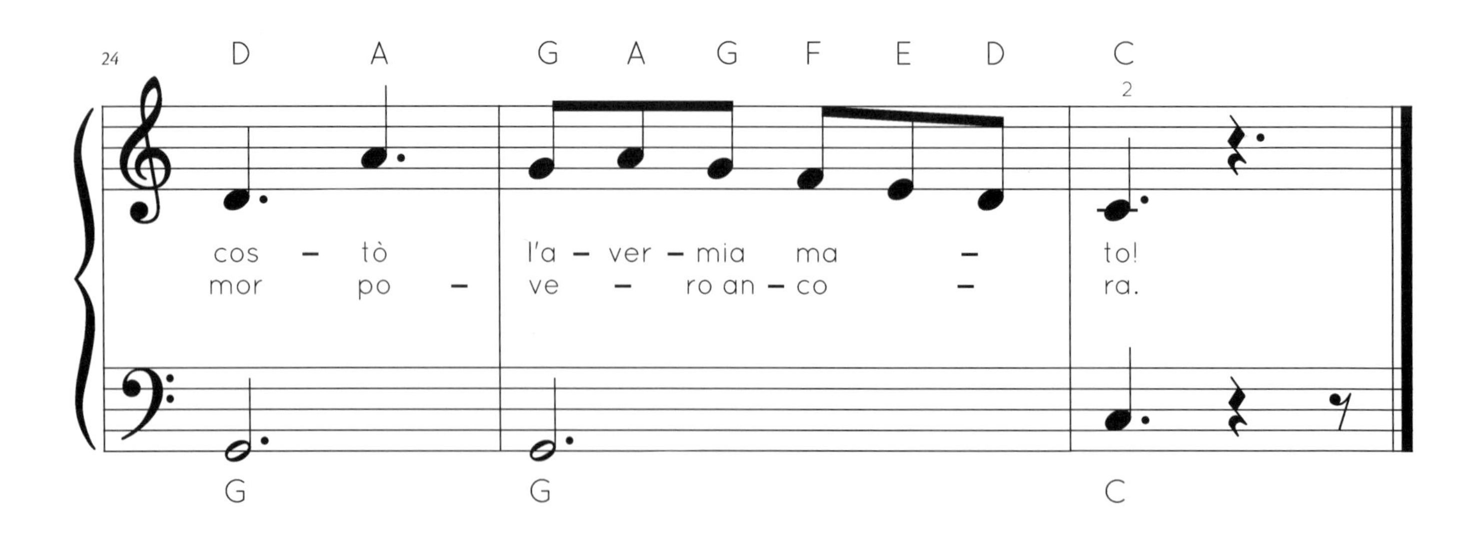
24
D A G A G F E D C
2
cos – tò l'a – ver – mia ma – to!
mor po – ve – ro an – co – ra.
G G C

While Shepherds Watched Their Flocks

Lyrics: Nahum Tate

Up on the Housetop

10
G G G E D D F E G G C E
Who would-n't go, ho, ho, ho! Who would-n't go!
C G C
13
G G A G E F G A
Up on the house - top click, click, click!
C F
15
G G A G E E D G C
Down thru the chim - ney with good Saint Nick.
C G C

Jolly Old Saint Nicholas

Christmas carol

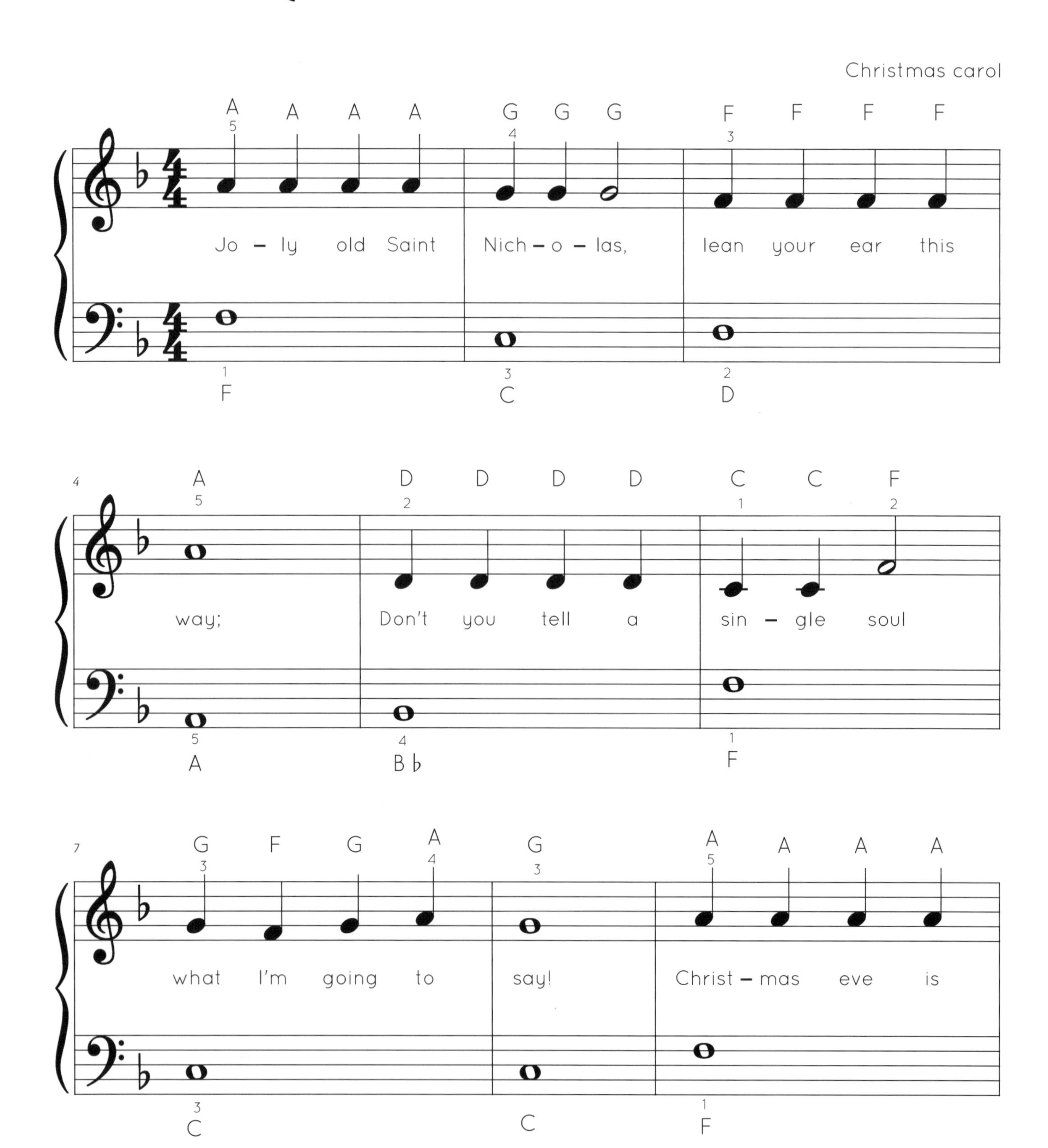

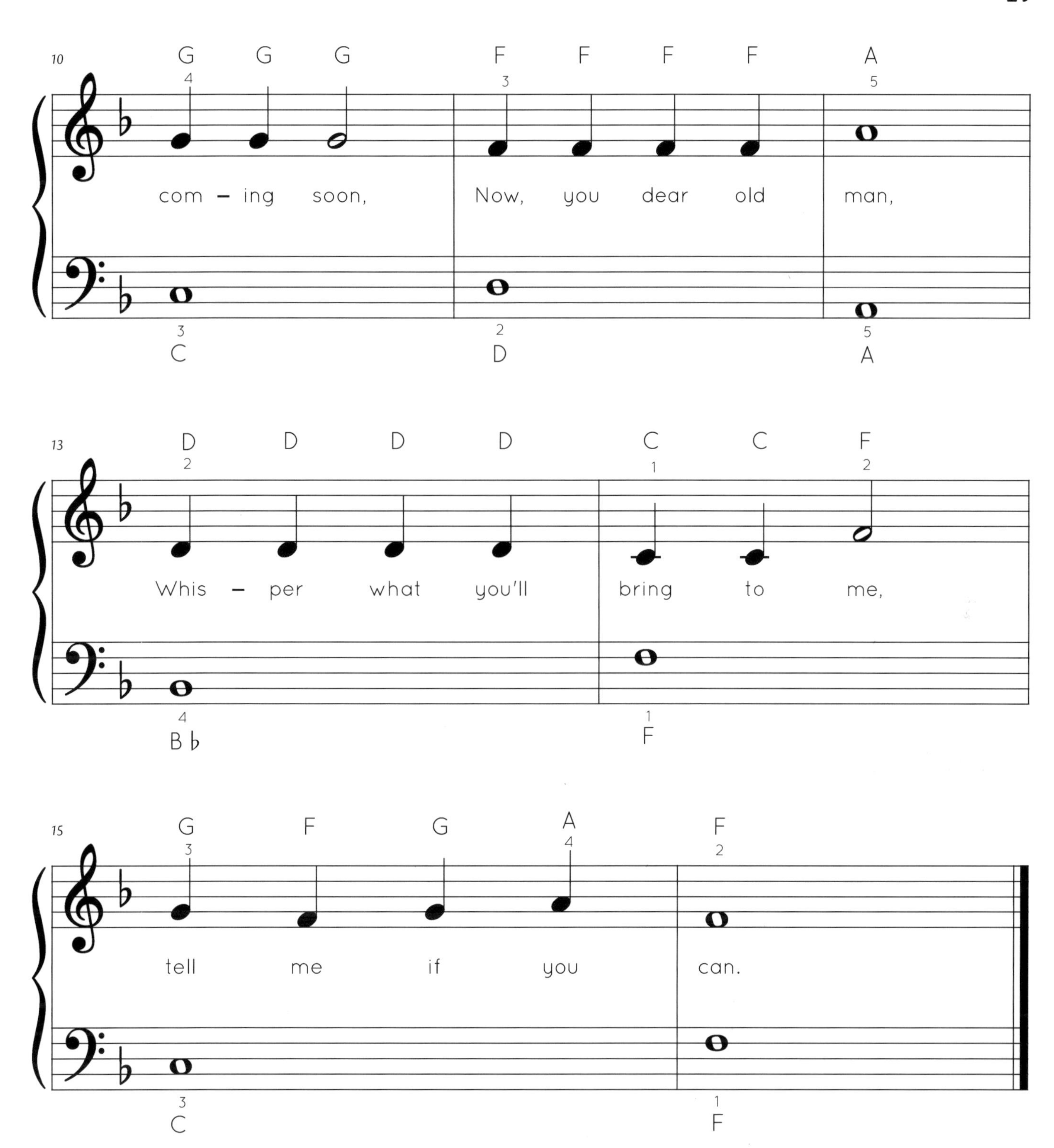
10
G G G F F F F A
4 3 5
com – ing soon, Now, you dear old man,
3 2 5
C D A
13
D D D D C C F
2 1 2
Whis – per what you'll bring to me,
4 1
B ♭ F
15
G F G A F
3 4 2
tell me if you can.
3 1
C F

Amazing Grace

Music: Traditional
Lyrics: John Newton

Hallelujah
(Messiah)

Georg Friedrich Händel

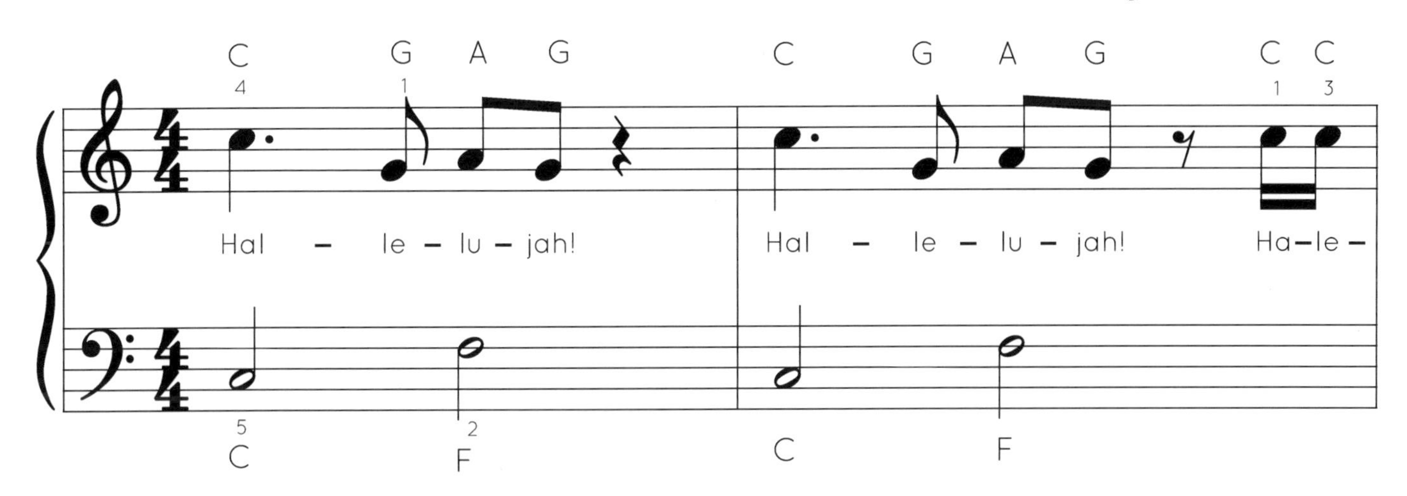

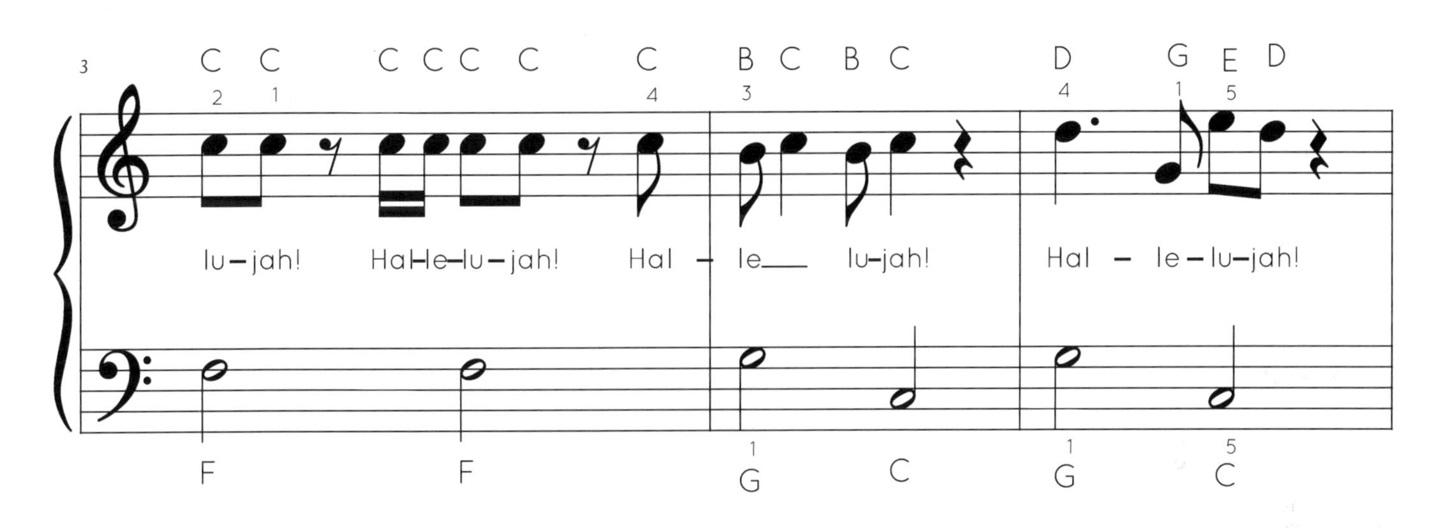

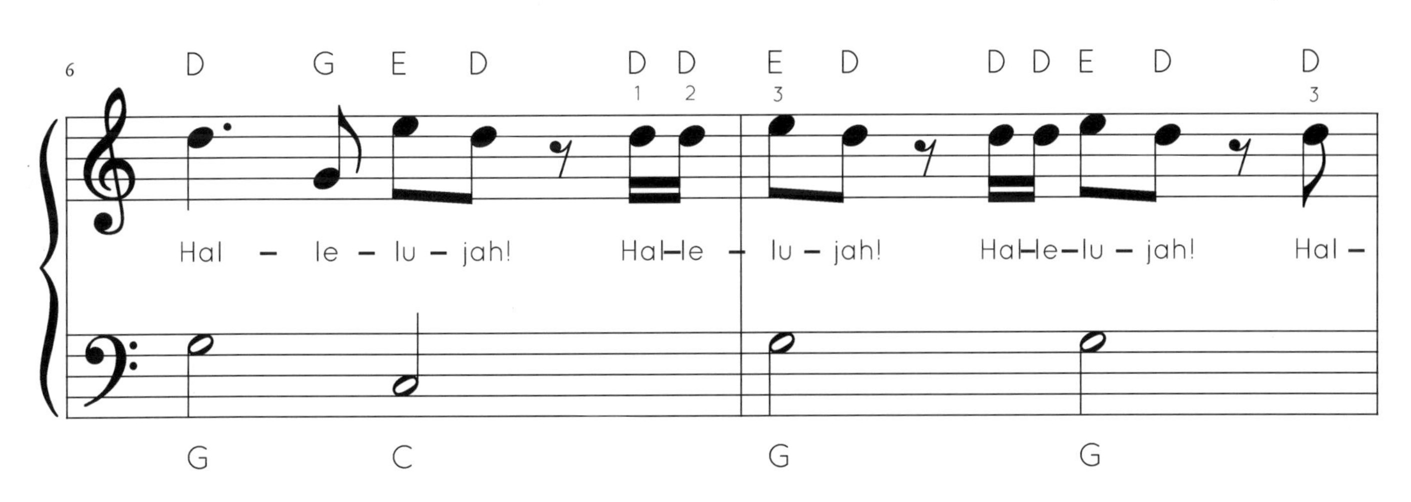

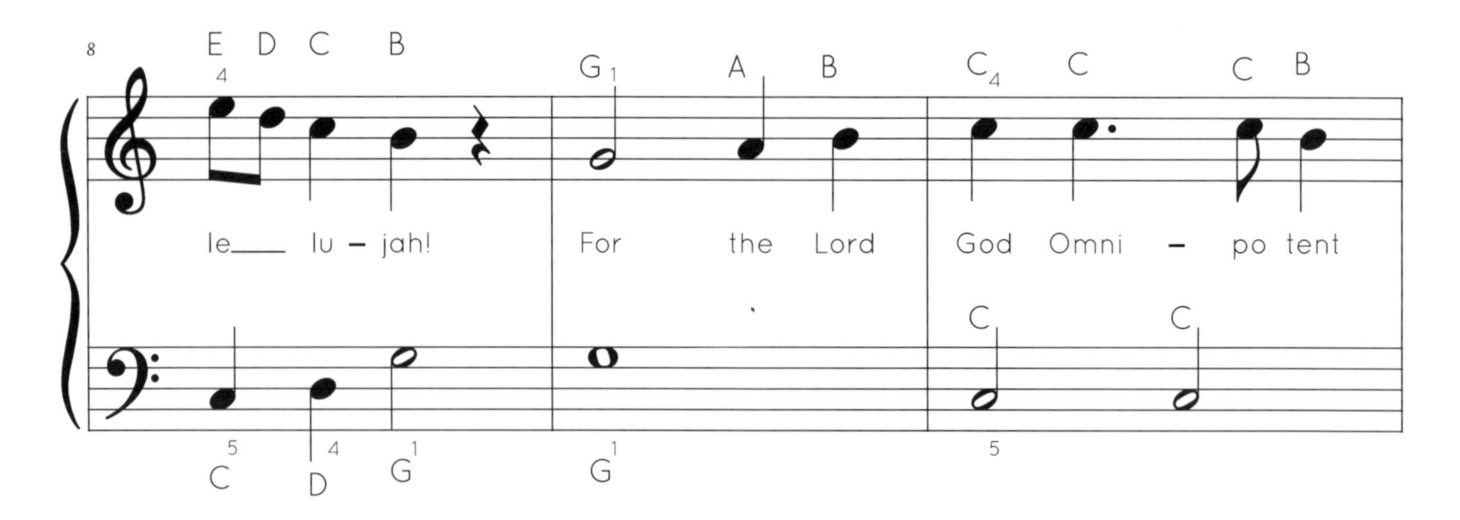
8
E D C B
4
G 1 A B
C 4 C C B
le___ lu – jah!
For the Lord
God Omni – po tent
C C
5 4 1
C D G
1
G
5

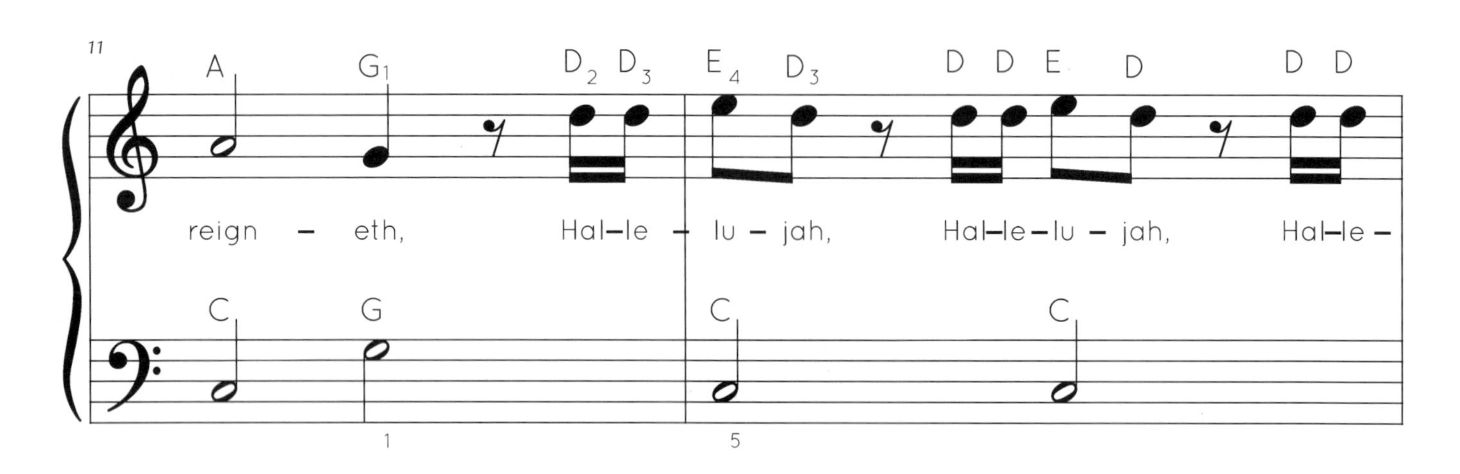
11
A G 1 D 2 D 3
E 4 D 3 D D E D D D
reign – eth, Hal–le – lu – jah, Hal–le–lu – jah, Hal–le –
C G
C C
1
5

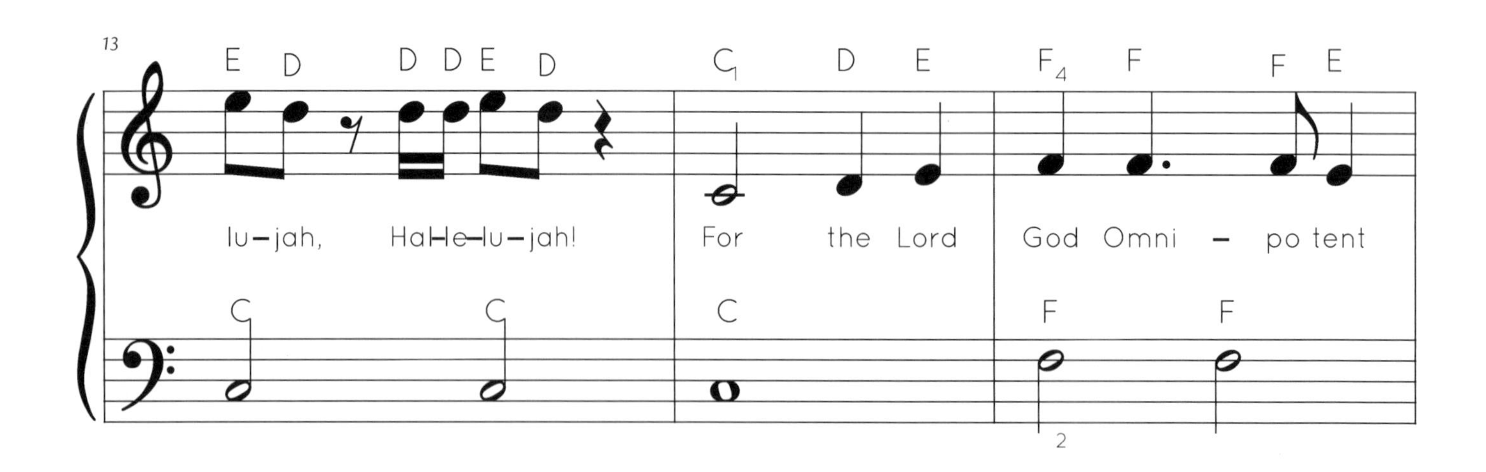
13
E D D D E D
C 1 D E
F 4 F F E
lu–jah, Hal–le–lu–jah!
For the Lord
God Omni – po tent
C C
C
F F
2

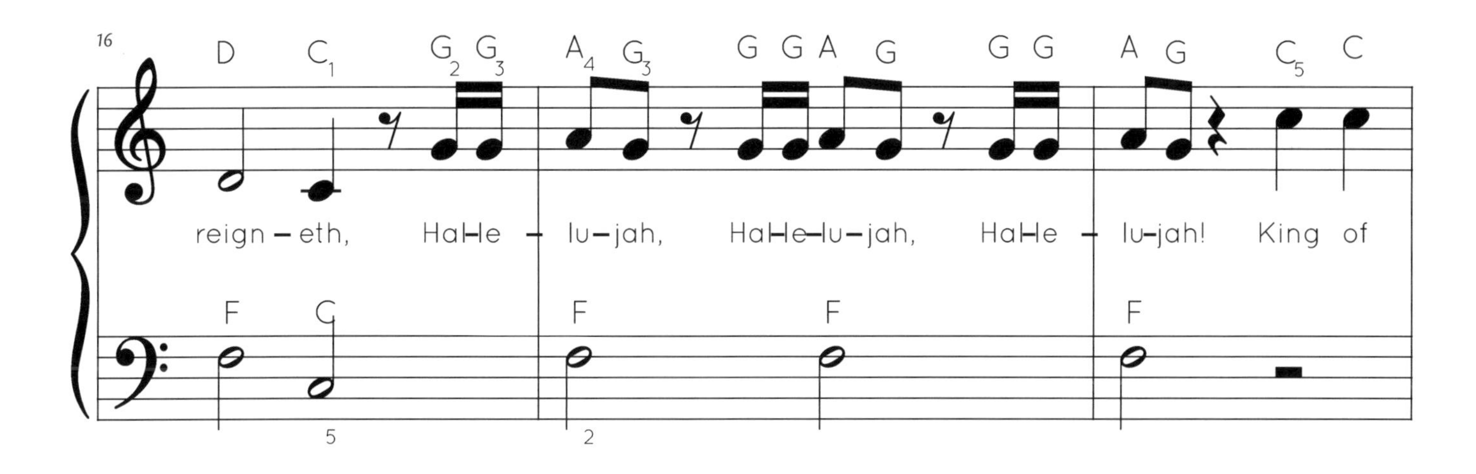
16
D C C G G A G G G A G G G A G C C
reign – eth, Hal-le – lu – jah, Hal-le-lu-jah, Hal-le – lu-jah! King of
F C F F F

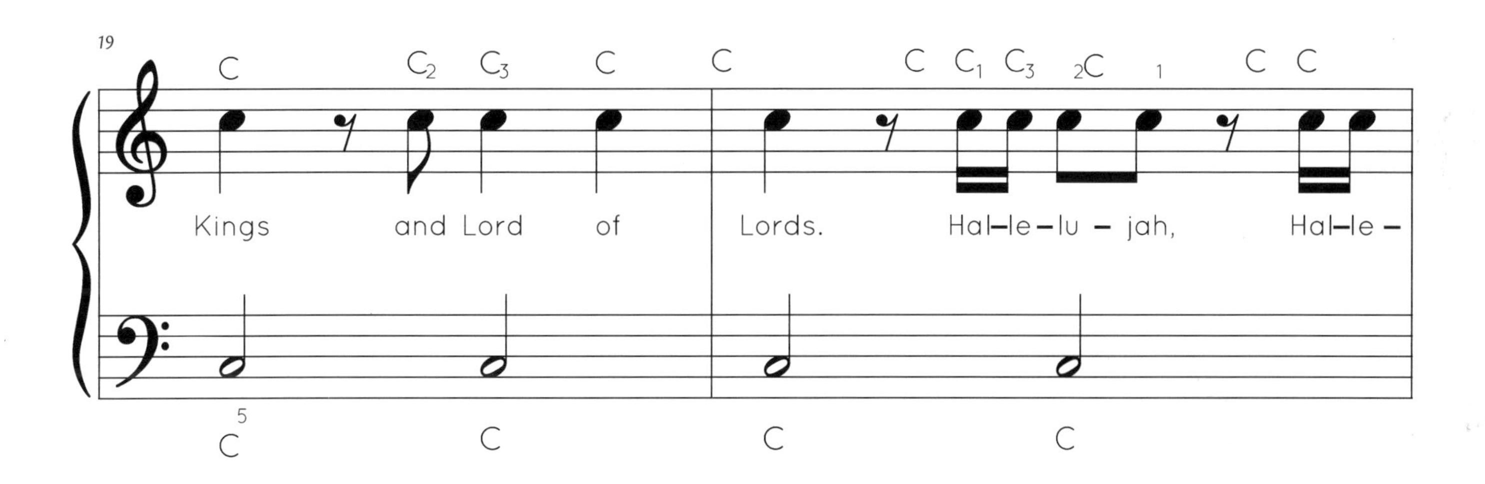
19
C C C C C C C C C C C C
Kings and Lord of Lords. Hal-le-lu – jah, Hal-le –
C C C C

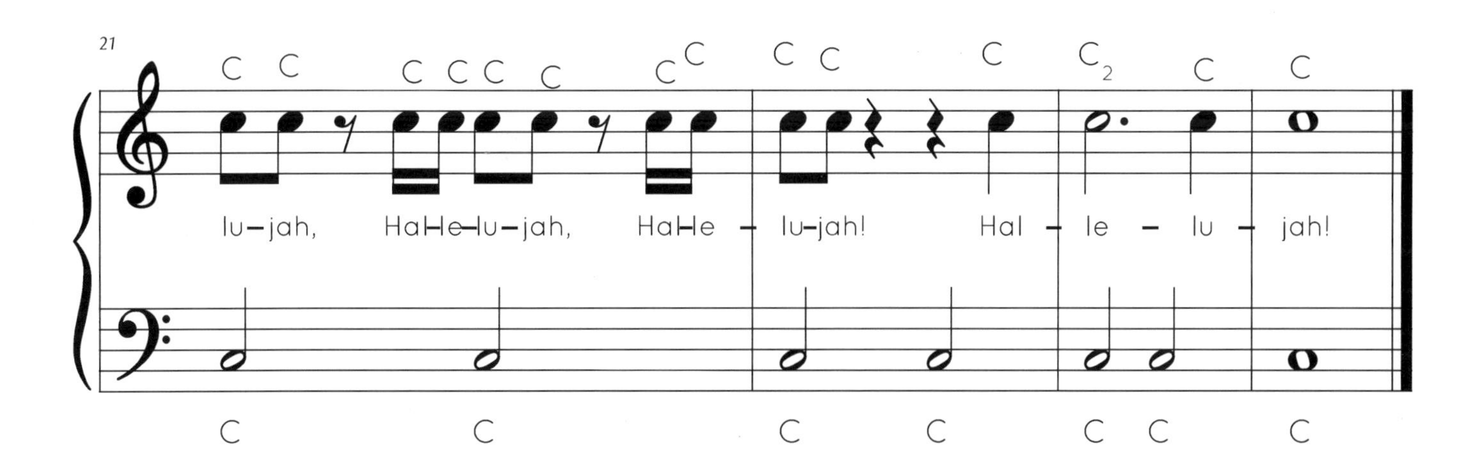
21
C C C C C C C C C C C C C C C
lu-jah, Hal-le-lu-jah, Hal-le – lu-jah! Hal – le – lu – jah!
C C C C C C C

Angels We Have Heard on High

Christmas carol

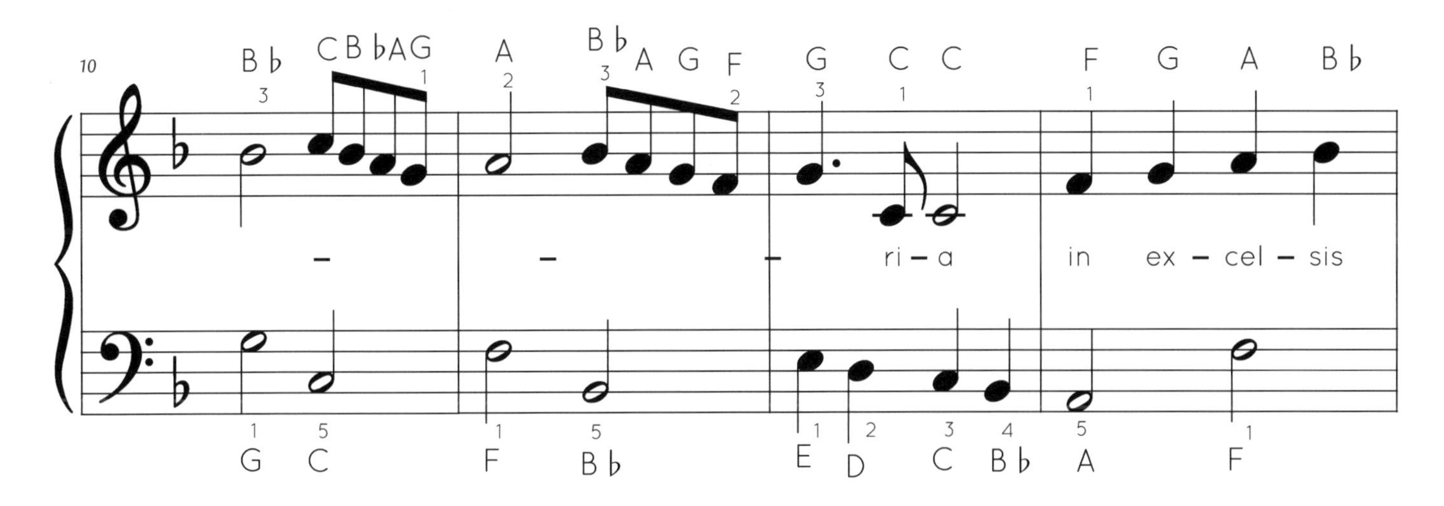
10
B♭ C B♭ A G A B♭ A G F G C C F G A B♭
3 1 2 3 2 3 1 1
– – – ri – a in ex – cel – sis
1 5 1 5 1 2 3 4 5 1
G C F B♭ E D C B♭ A F

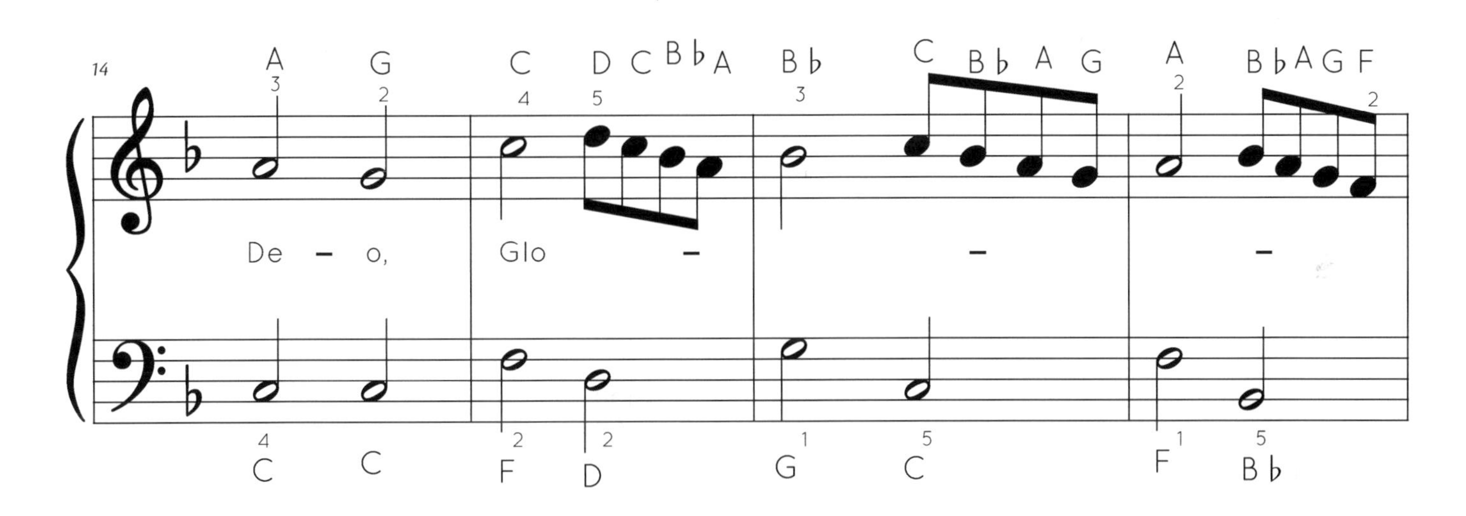
14
A G C D C B♭ A B♭ C B♭ A G A B♭ A G F
3 2 4 5 3 2 2
De – o, Glo – – –
4 2 2 1 5 1 5
C C F D G C F B♭

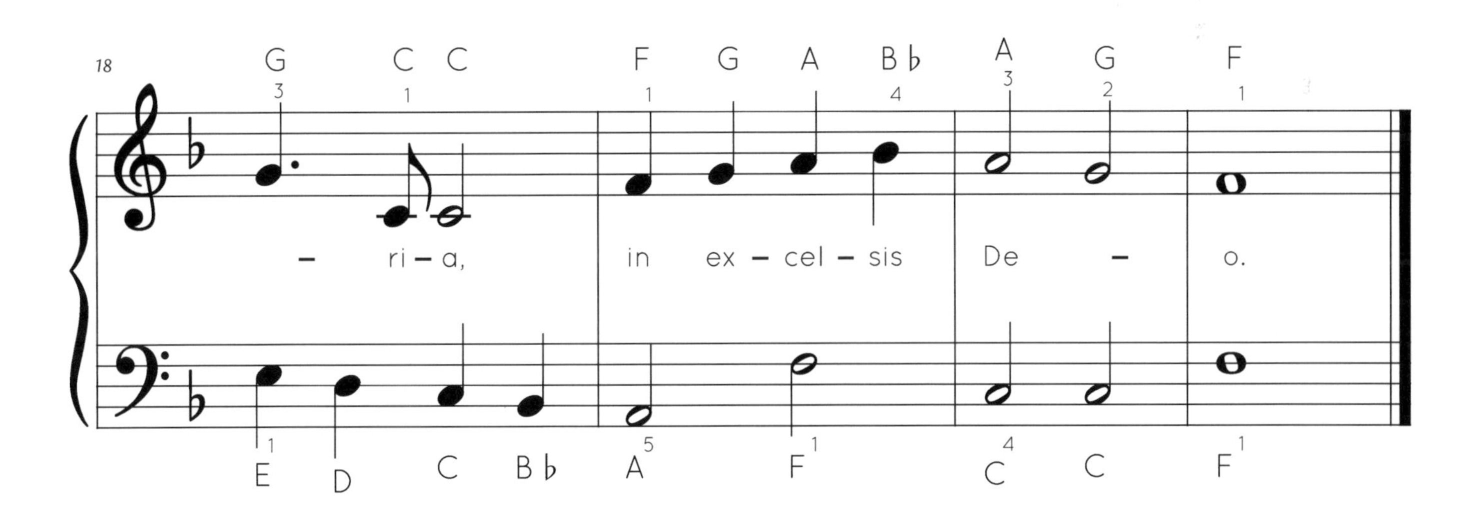
18
G C C F G A B♭ A G F
3 1 1 4 3 2 1
– ri – a, in ex – cel – sis De – o.
1 5 1 4 1
E D C B♭ A F C C F

Ding! Dong! Merrily on High

Lyrics: George Ratcliffe Woodward

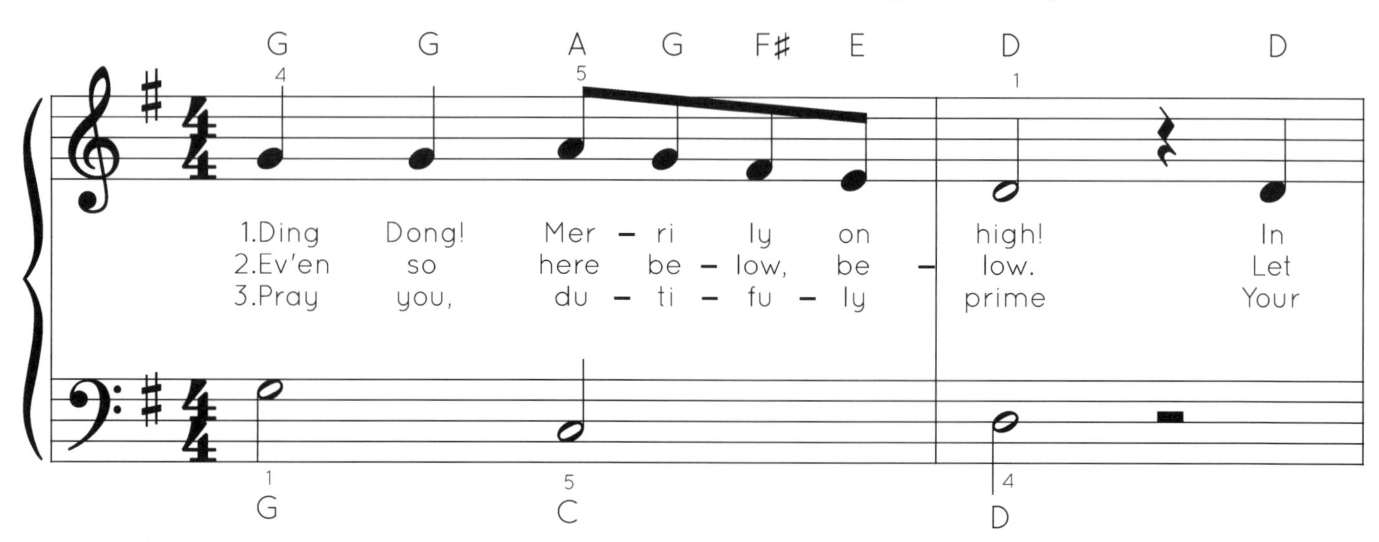

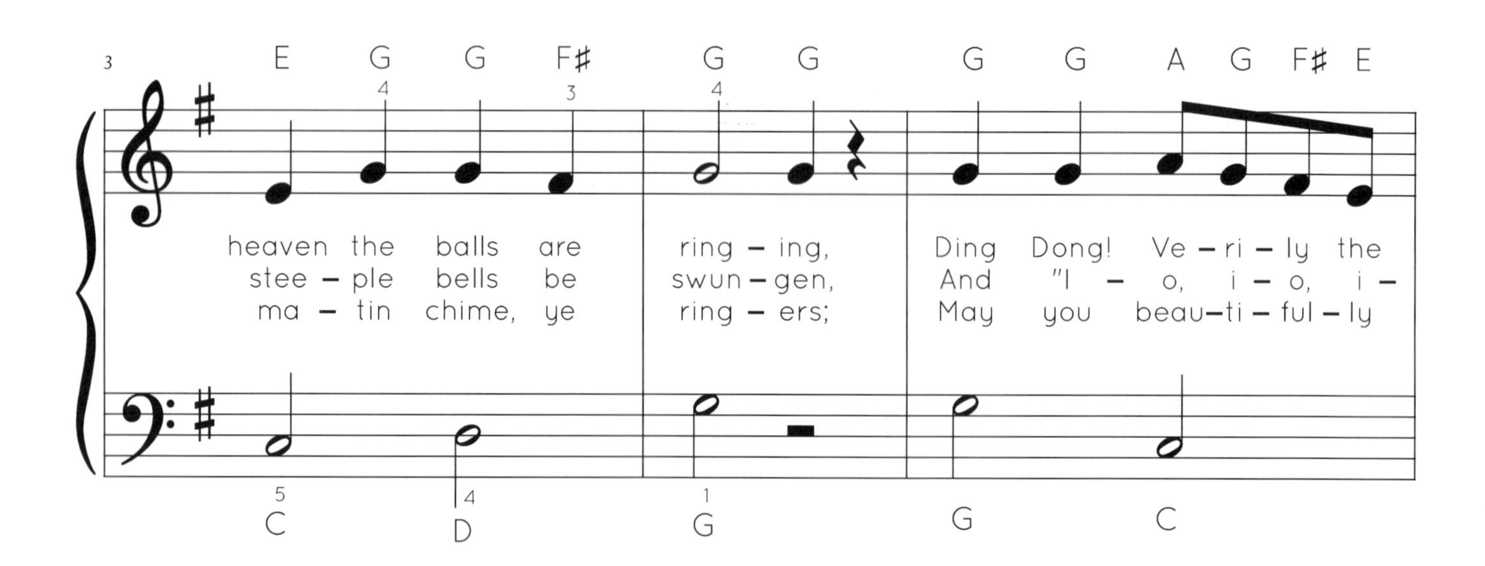

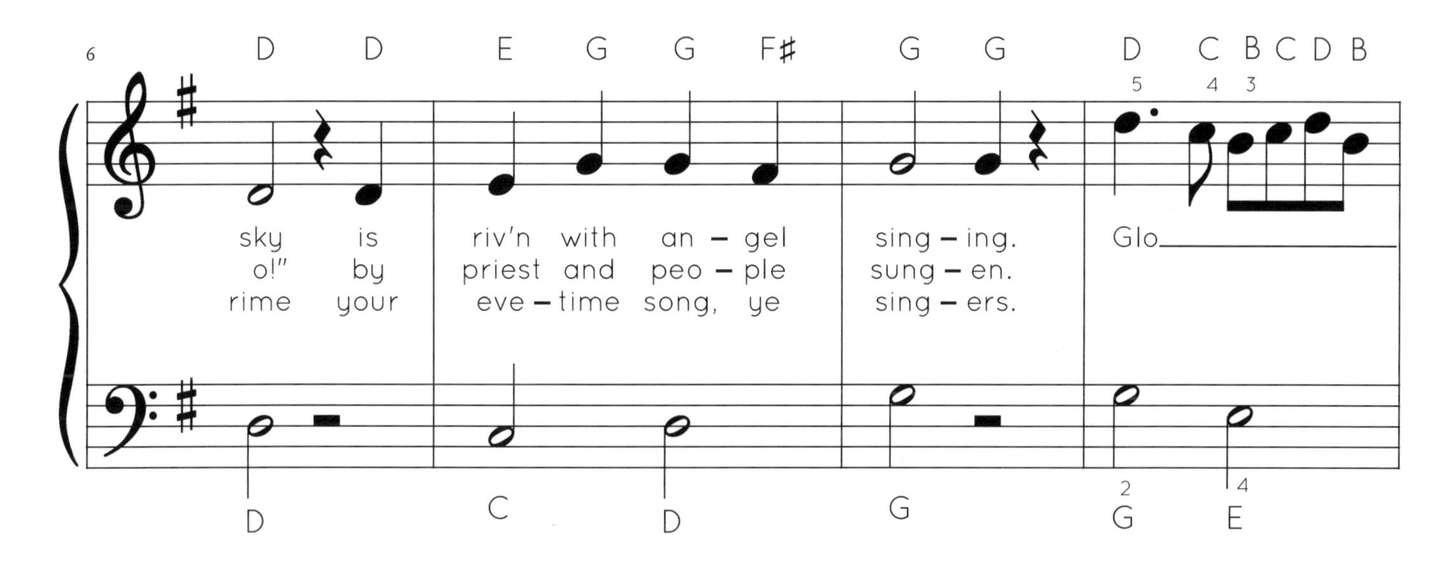
6
D D E G G F♯ G G D C B C D B
5 4 3
sky is riv'n with an – gel sing – ing. Glo
o!" by priest and peo – ple sung – en.
rime your eve – time song, ye sing – ers.
D C D G G E
2 4

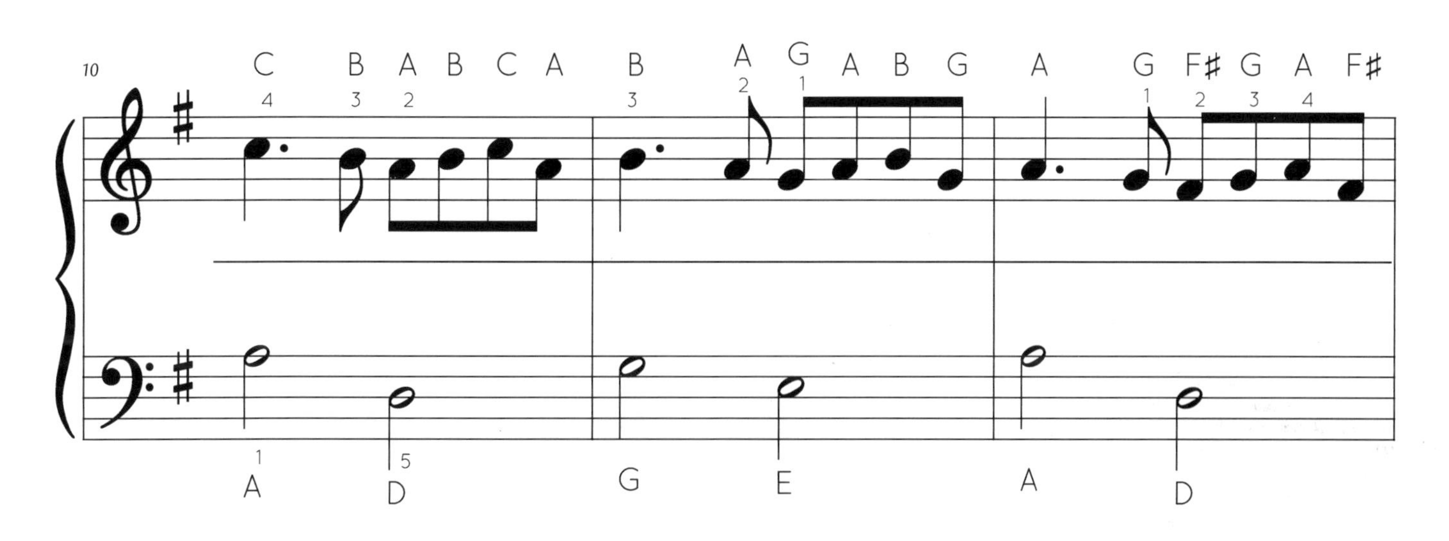
10
C B A B C A B A G A B G A G F♯ G A F♯
4 3 2 3 2 1 1 2 3 4
1 5
A D G E A D

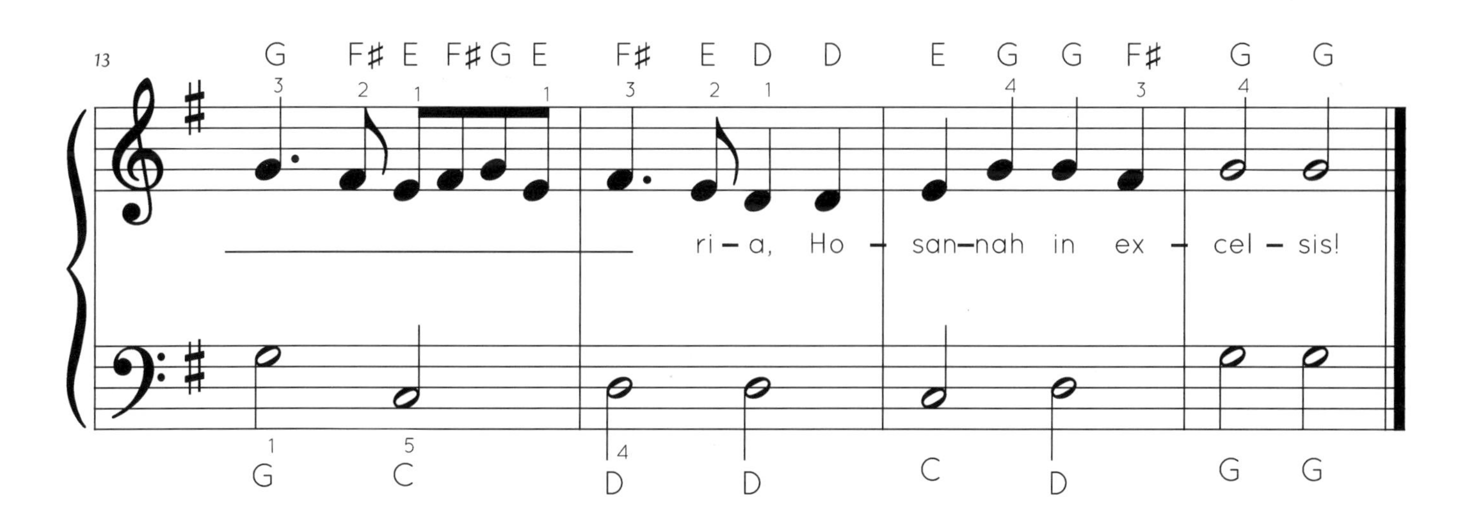
13
G F♯ E F♯ G E F♯ E D D E G G F♯ G G
3 2 1 1 3 2 1 4 3 4
ri – a, Ho – san–nah in ex – cel – sis!
1 5 4
G C D D C D G G

God Rest You Merry, Gentlemen

Christmas carol

9
C A B C D E B A G E F♯ G
save us all from Sa – tan's pow'r when we were gone a –
that in Beth – le – hem was born the Son of God by
free all those who trust in Him from Sa – tan's pow'r and
A G B G A A
12
A G A B C B B A G F♯ E G F♯ E
stray, O___ ti – dings of com___ fort and joy, com–fort and
Name,
might."
D G C G B E E
16
A G A B C D E B A G F♯ E
joy; O___ ti – dings of com – fort and joy.
D C B A G B C G A B D♯ E

Hark! The Herald Angels Sing

Music: Felix Mendelssohn
Lyrics: Charles Wesley

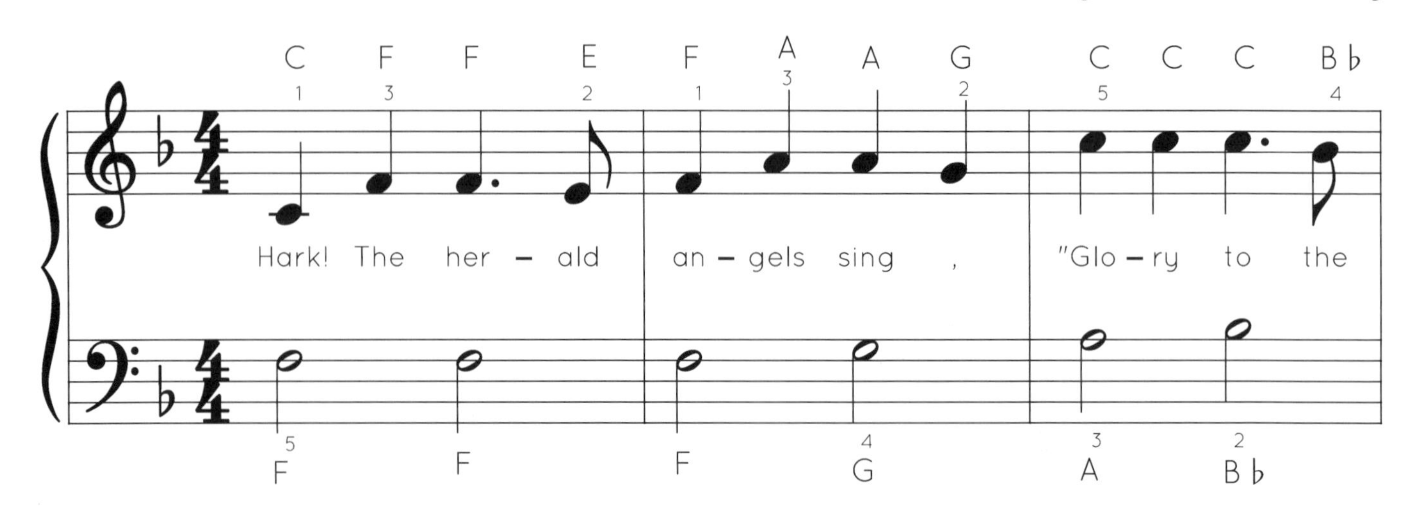

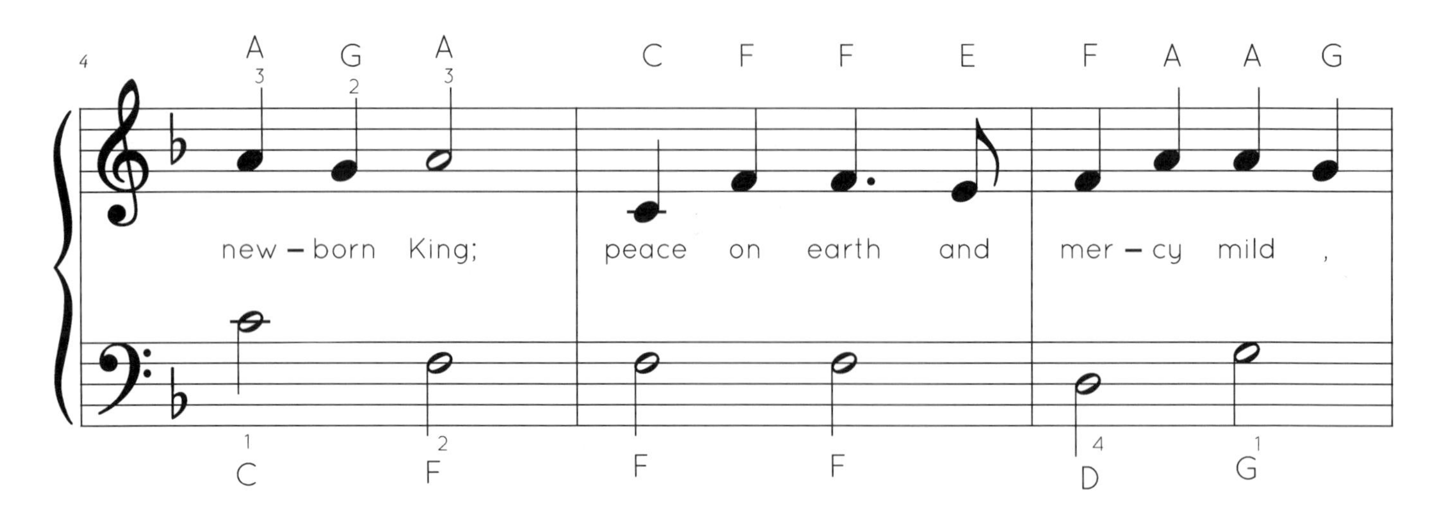

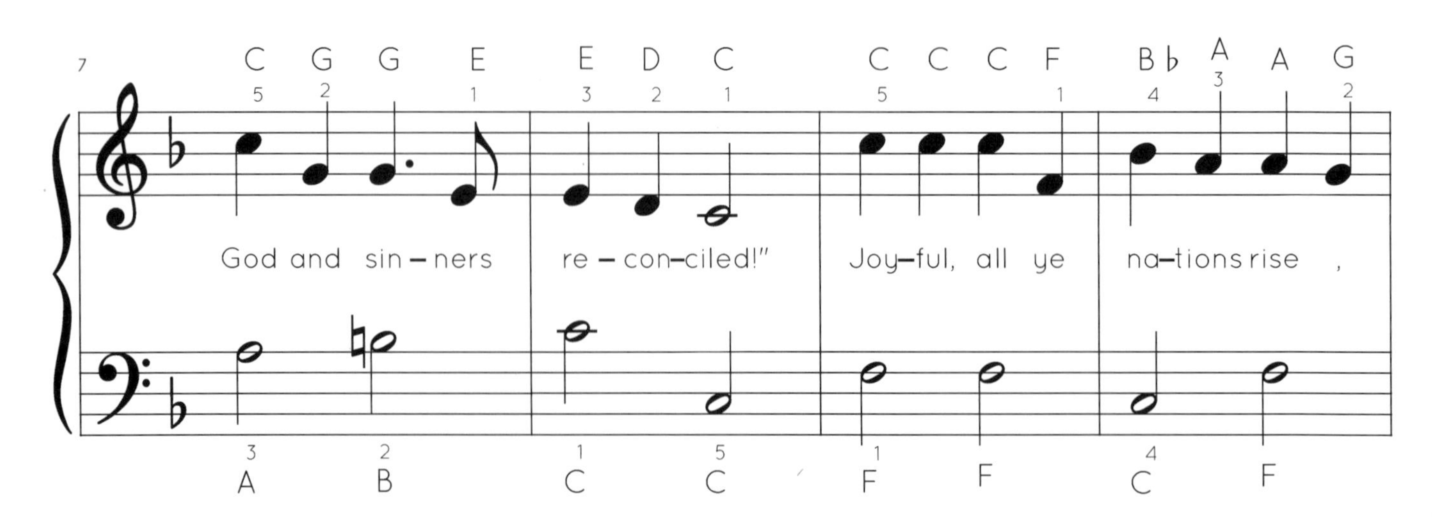

11
C C C F B♭ A A G D D D C B♭ A B♭
join the tri–umph of the skies ; with an–ge–lic host pro–claim;
F F C F B♭ B♭ G G
15
G A B♭ C F F G A D D D C
"Christ is born in Beth – le – hem!" Hark! The her – ald
C B♭ A F B♭ B♭
18
B♭ A B♭ G A B♭ C F F G F
an – gels sing, "Glo – ry to the new–born King!
G G C B♭ A C F

It Came Upon the Midnight Clear

Music: Richard Storrs Willis
Lyrics: Edmund H. Sears

9
E D E G F E D A
on earth___ good will to men, from
bove its sad and low – ly plans they
man at war with man hears not the
A A
11
G F E D C C C B♭ A G A
heaven's all gra – cious King!" The world in so – lemn_
bend on hov – 'ring wing; and ev – er o'er its___
love – song wich they bring; O hush the noise ye___
G C A
14
B♭ A G F G A B♭ C A G F
still – ness lay to___ hear_ the an – gels sing.
Ba – bel sounds the___ bless – ed an – gels sing.
men of strife, and___ hear_ the an – gels sing.
G C F

O Christmas Tree
(O Tannenbaum)

German Christmas song

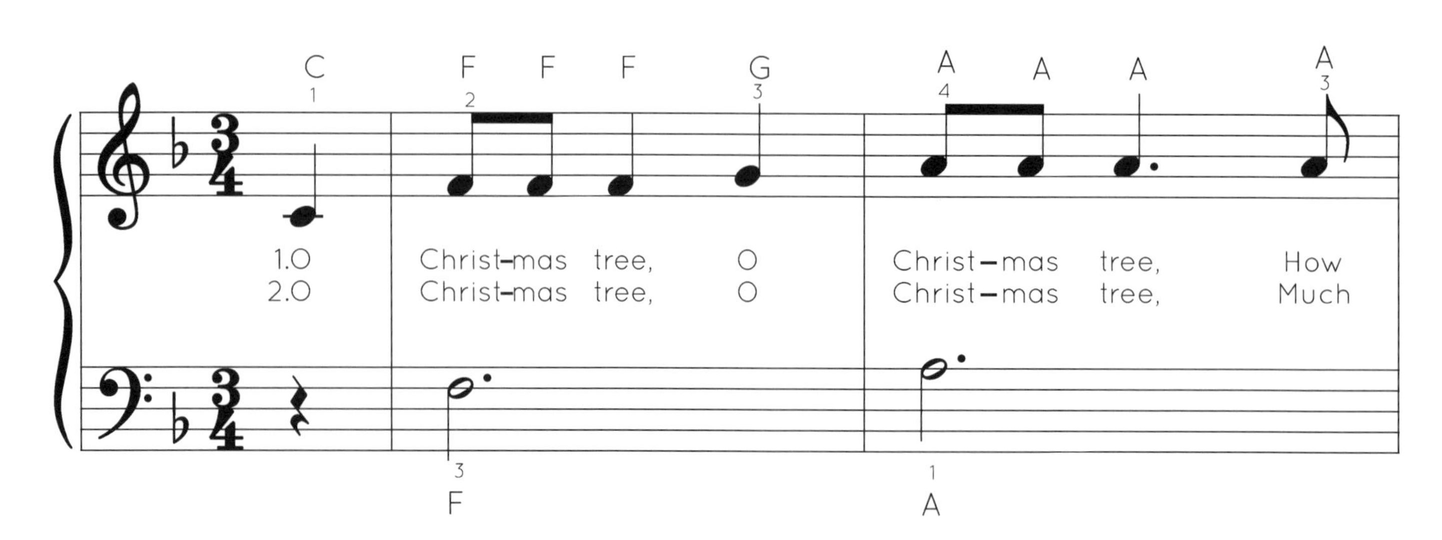

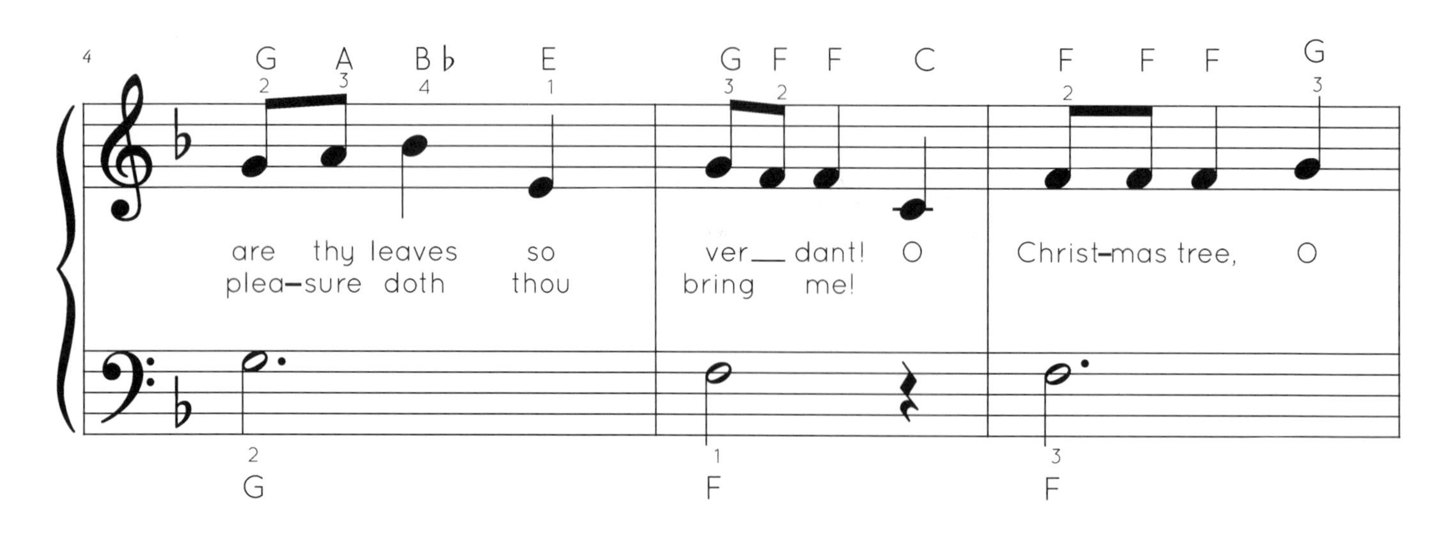

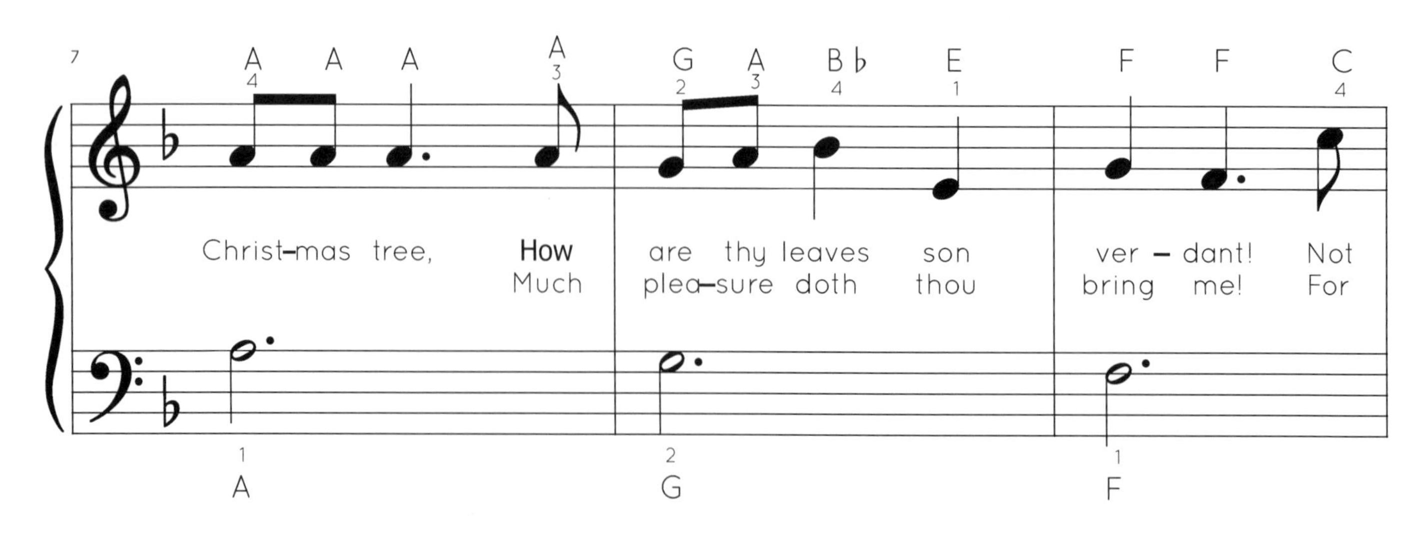

10
C A D C C B♭ B♭ B♭ B♭ G C B♭
on – ly in the sum – mer time, But ev'n in win – ter,
ev – ery year the Christ–mas tree, Brings to us all both
A B♭ E C
13
B♭ A A C F F F G A A A A
is thy prime. O Christ–mas tree, O Christ–mass tree, How
joy and glee. Much
F F A
16
G A B♭ E F F
are thy leaves so ver – dant!
plea – sure doth thou bring me!
G F

O Come, All Ye Faithful

(Adeste Fideles)

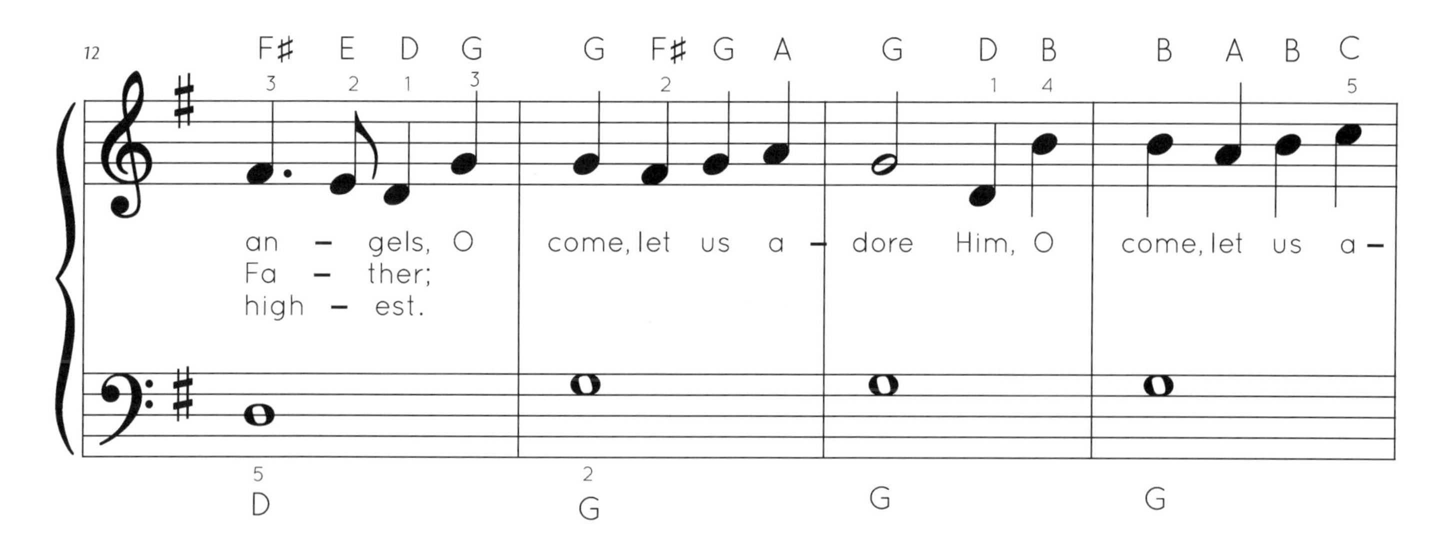
12
F♯ E D G G F♯ G A G D B B A B C
3 2 1 3 2 1 4 5
an – gels, O come, let us a – dore Him, O come, let us a –
Fa – ther;
high – est.
5 2
D G G G

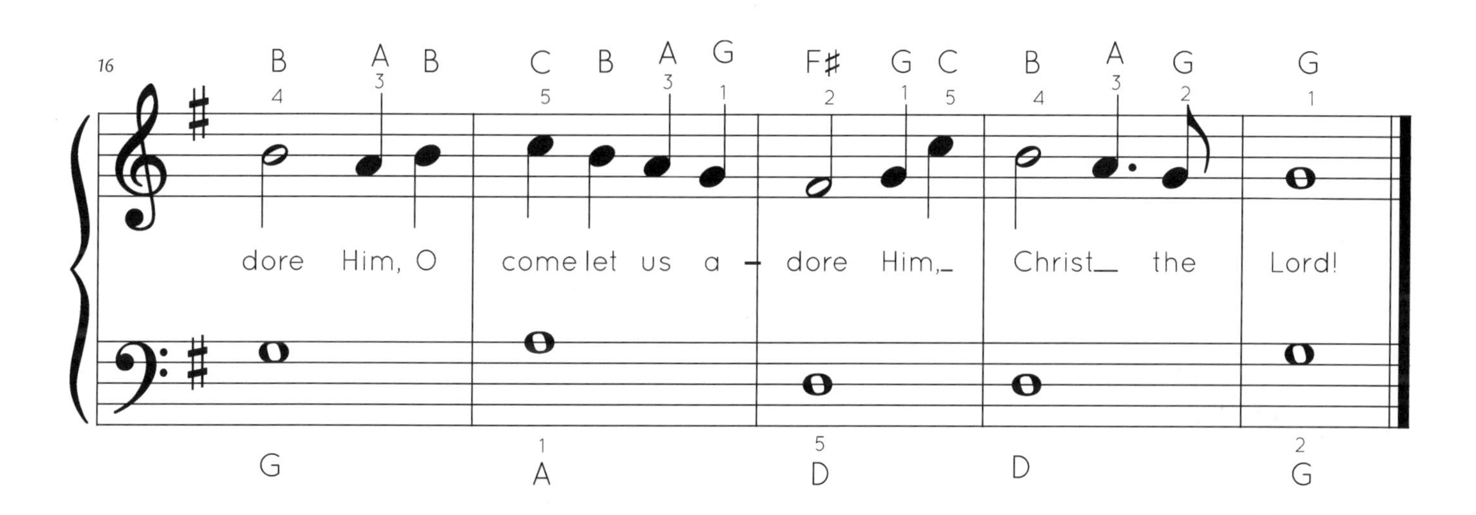
16
B A B C B A G F♯ G C B A G G
4 3 5 3 1 2 1 5 4 3 2 1
dore Him, O come let us a – dore Him,_ Christ_ the Lord!
1 5 2
G A D D G

O Come, O Come, Emmanuel

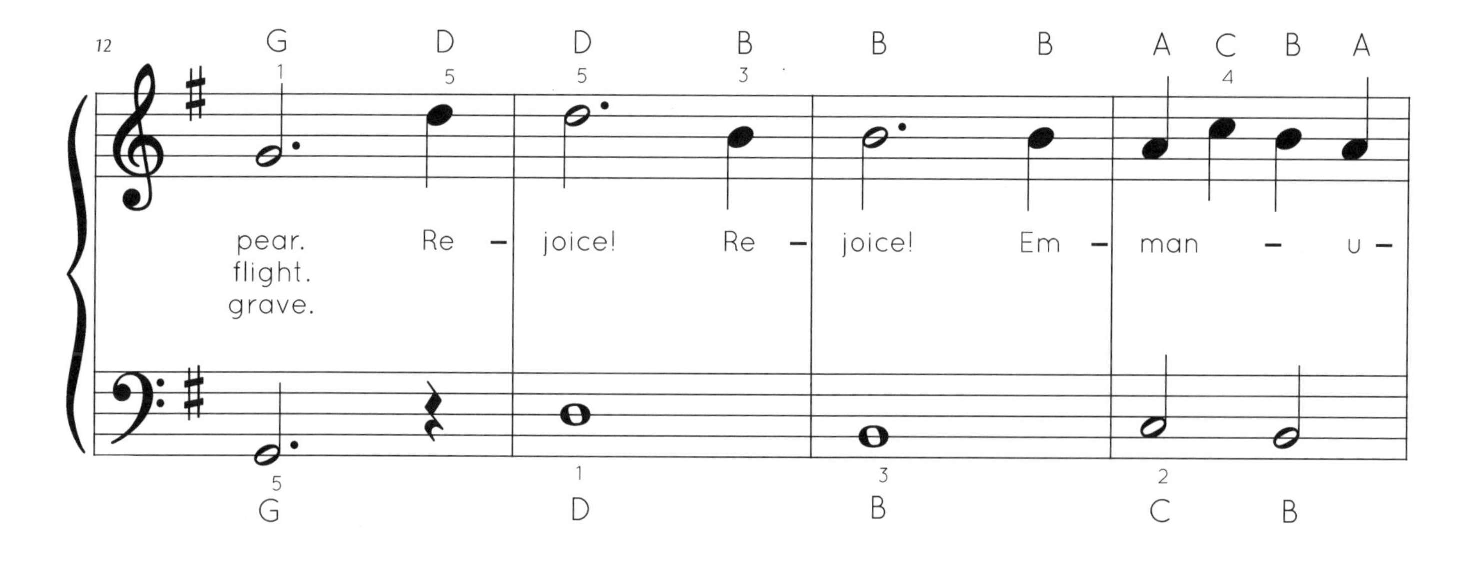
12
G D D B B B A C B A
1 5 5 3 4
pear. Re – joice! Re – joice! Em – man – u –
flight.
grave.
5 1 3 2
G D B C B

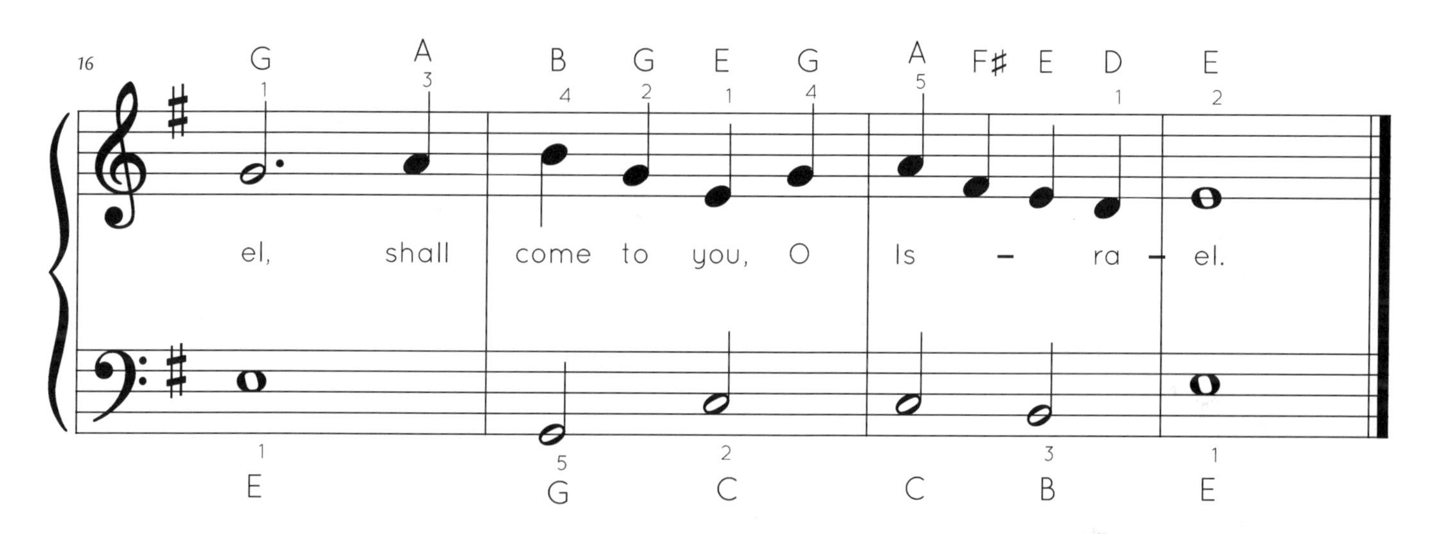
16
G A B G E G A F♯ E D E
1 3 4 2 1 4 5 1 2
el, shall come to you, O Is – ra – el.
1 5 2 3 1
E G C C B E

O Little Town of Bethlehem

Lyrics: Phillips Brooks

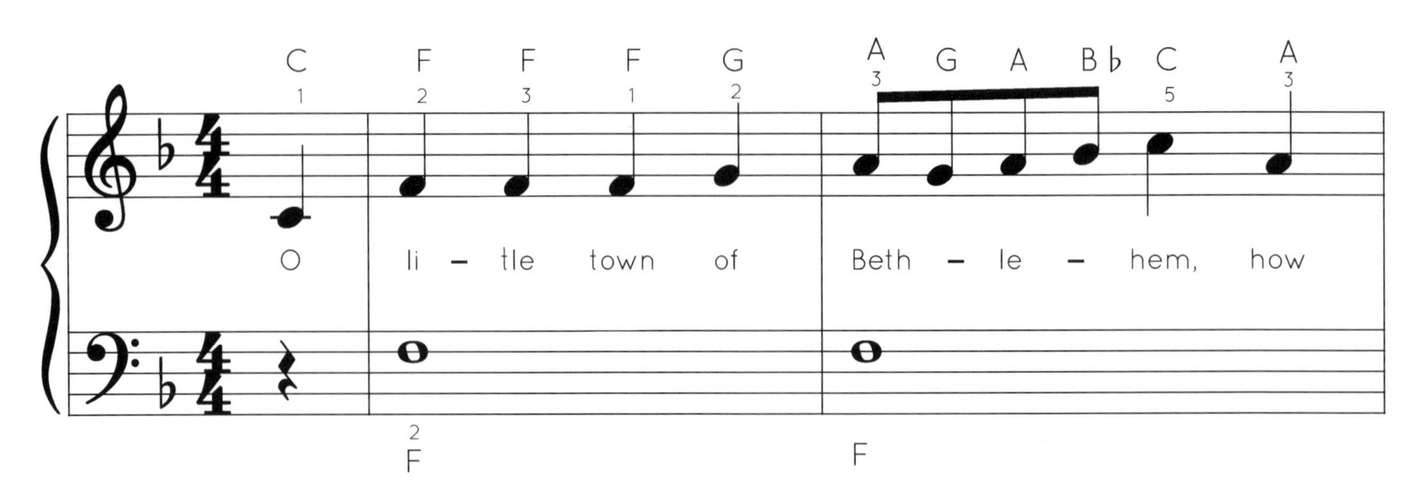

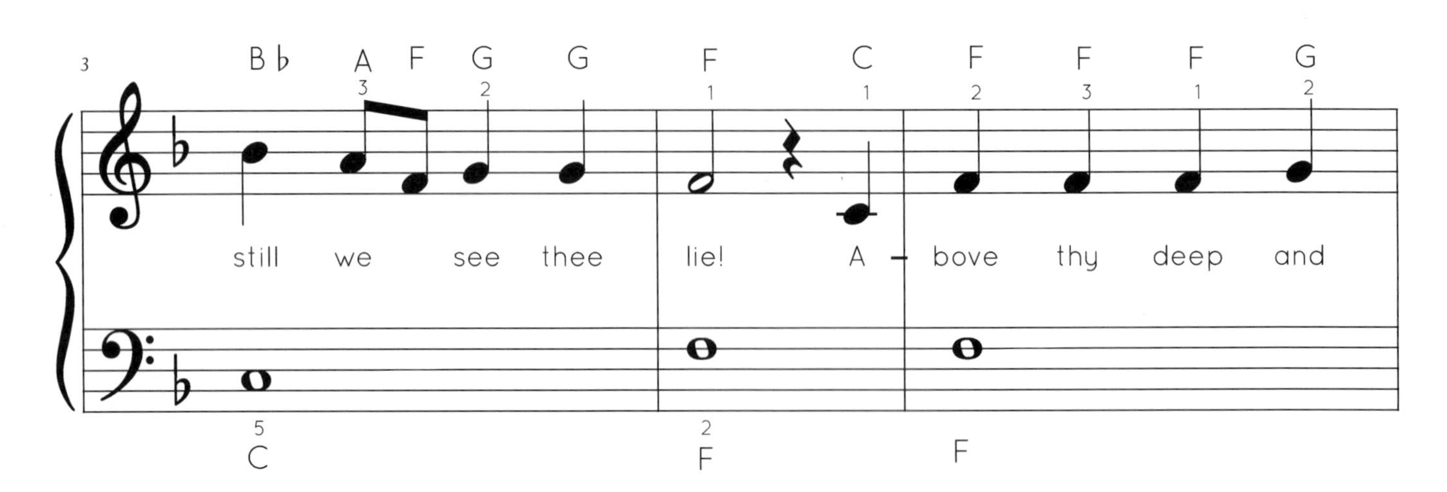

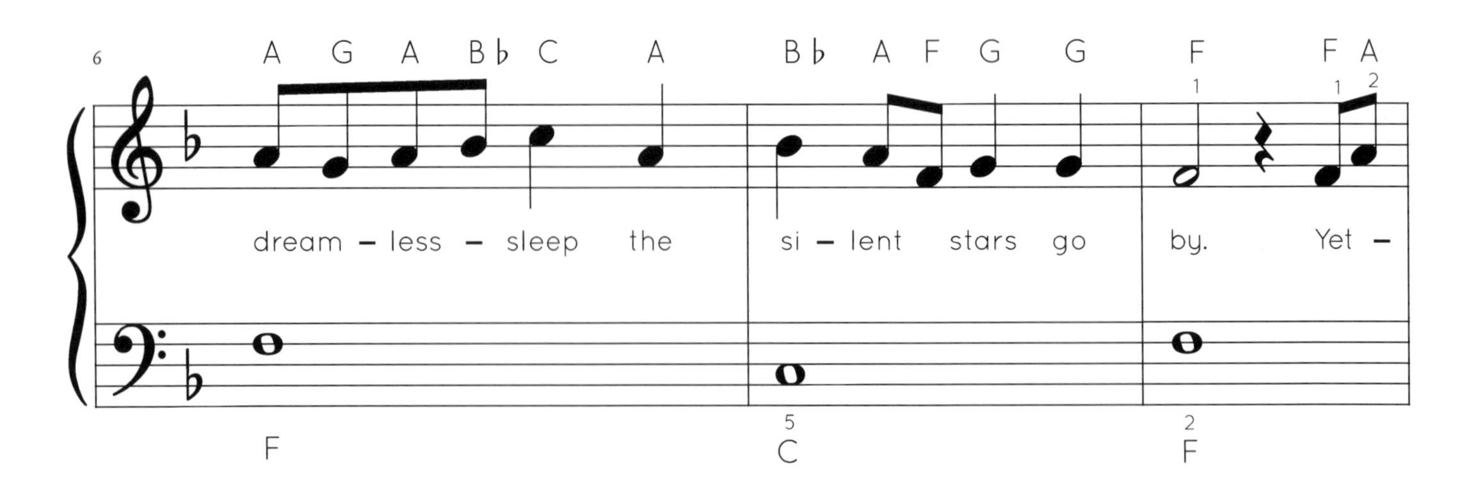

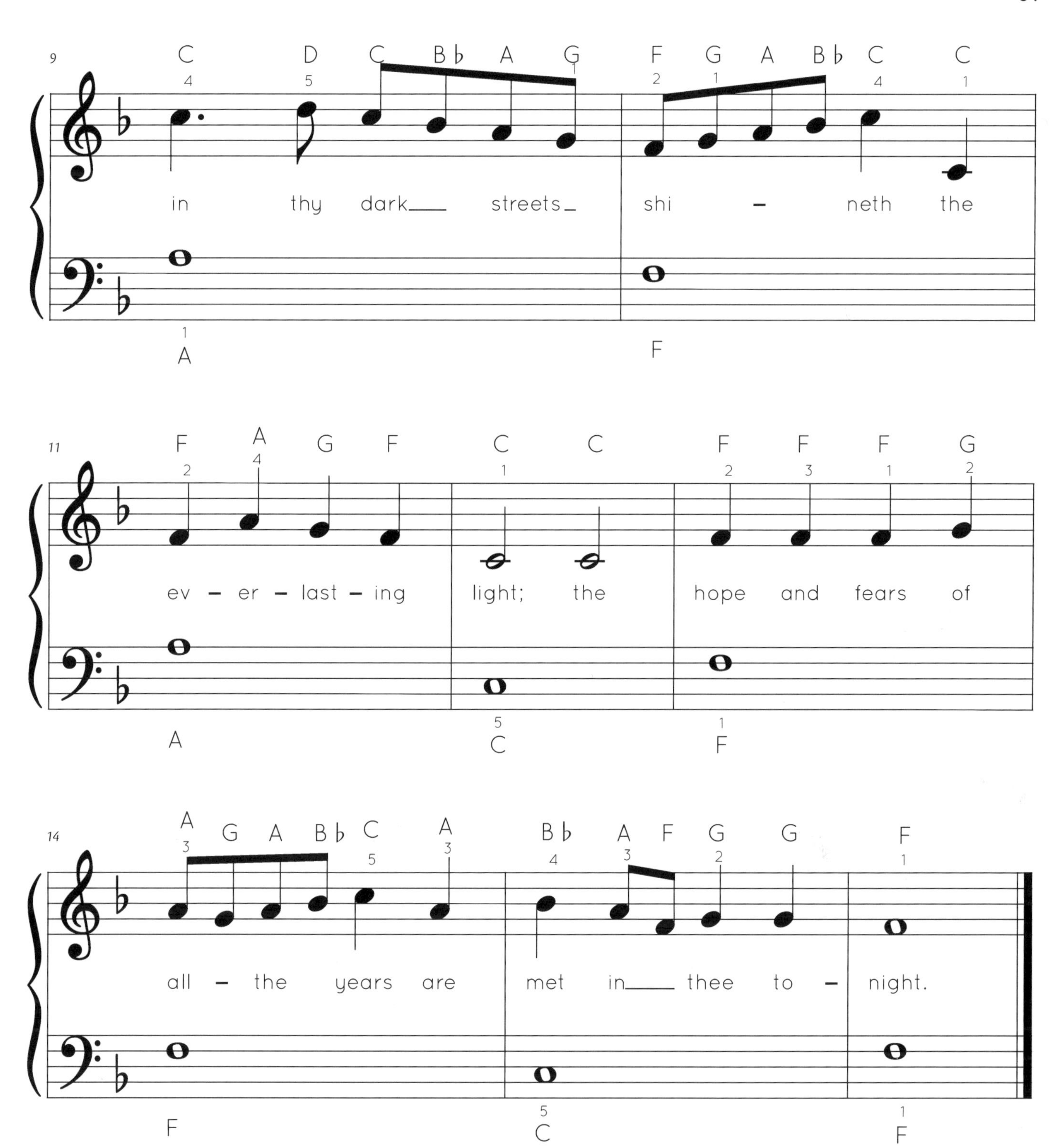
9
C D C B♭ A G F G A B♭ C C
in thy dark__ streets_ shi – neth the
A F
11
F A G F C C F F F G
ev – er – last – ing light; the hope and fears of
A C F
14
A G A B♭ C A B♭ A F G G F
all – the years are met in__ thee to – night.
F C F

Pat-a-pan

Music and lyrics: Bernard de La Monnoye

6
C A B C D E D E D C
on? Tu – re – lu – re – lu, pa – ta – pa – ta –
on
on!
A A A A
8
B B C B G♯ A B
pan; When you play the fife and
And al – so the drums they'd
As the ins – tru – ments you
G♯ G♯ E E
10
C B C D C B E B A
drum, How can an – y one be glum?
play, Full of joy, on Christ – mas day.
play, We will sing this Christ – mas day.
A A E G♯ A

Silent Night

Music: Franz Xaver Gruber
Lyrics: Joseph Mohr

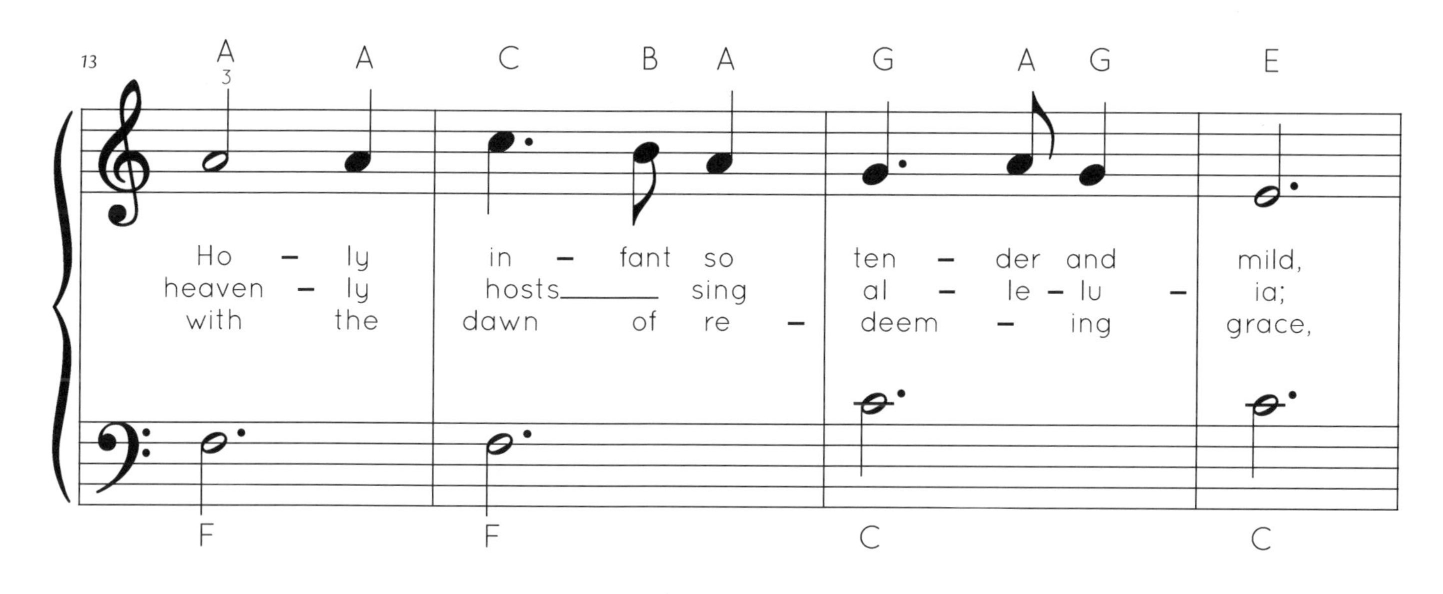
13
A A C B A G A G E
3
Ho - ly in - fant so ten - der and mild,
heaven - ly hosts sing al - le - lu - ia;
with the dawn of re - deem - ing grace,
F F C C

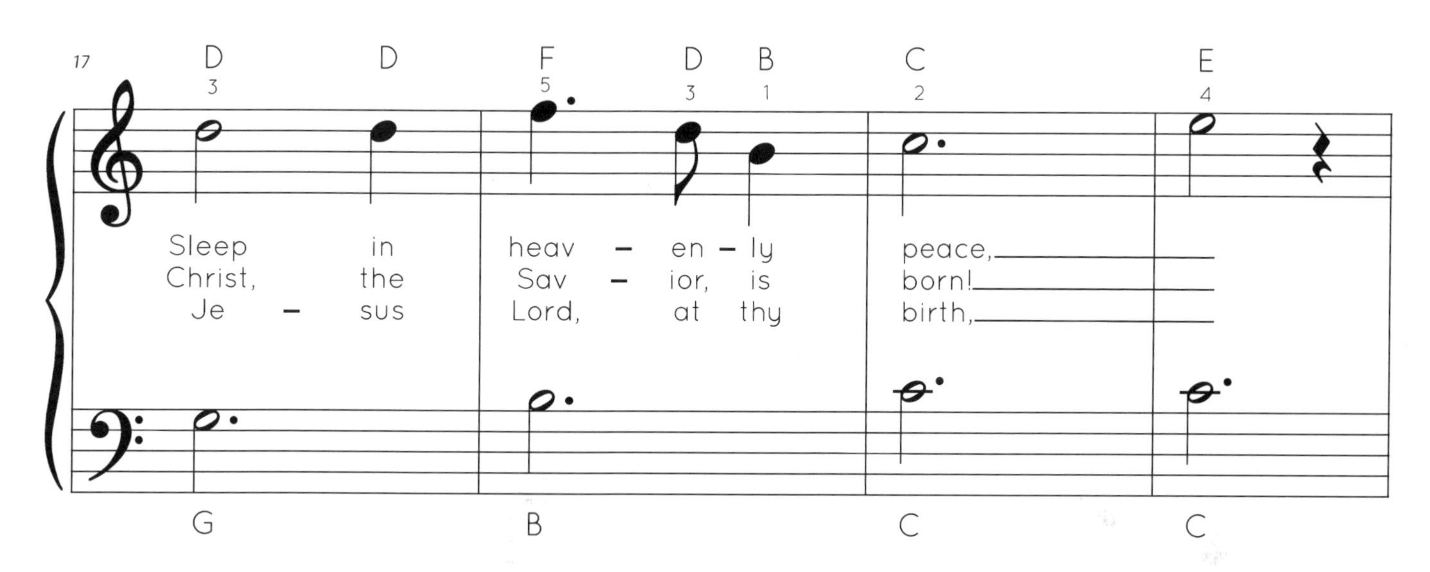
17
D D F D B C E
3 5 3 1 2 4
Sleep in heav - en - ly peace,
Christ, the Sav - ior, is born!
Je - sus Lord, at thy birth,
G B C C

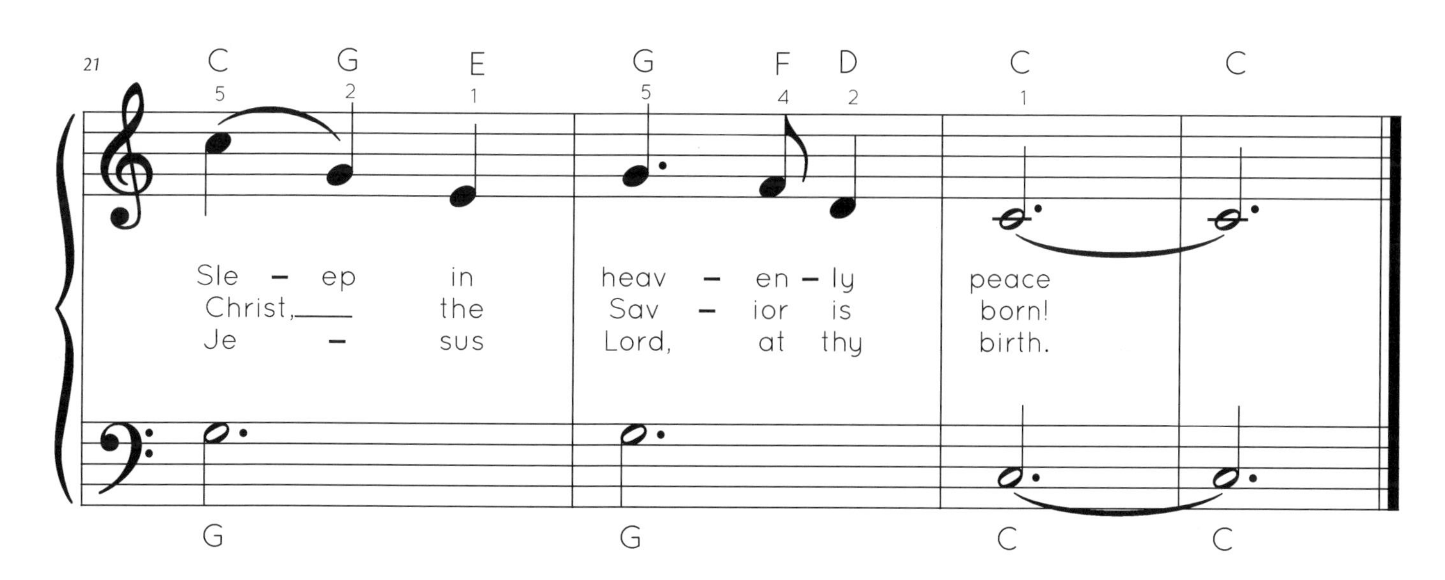
21
C G E G F D C C
5 2 1 5 4 2 1
Sle - ep in heav - en - ly peace
Christ, the Sav - ior is born!
Je - sus Lord, at thy birth.
G G C C

The First Noël

Christmas carol

13
G A B C B A G A B C G F
sheep on a cold win – ter's night that was so
light, and so it con – tin – ued both day and
tent, and to fol – low the star where – ev – er it
C F C F
17
E E D C D E F G C B A A G
deep. No__ el, no – el, no – el, no – el.
night.
went.
C C E F C
22
C B A G A B C G F E
Born is the King – of Is – ra el.
F C F C

I Heard the Bells on Christmas Day

Christmas carol

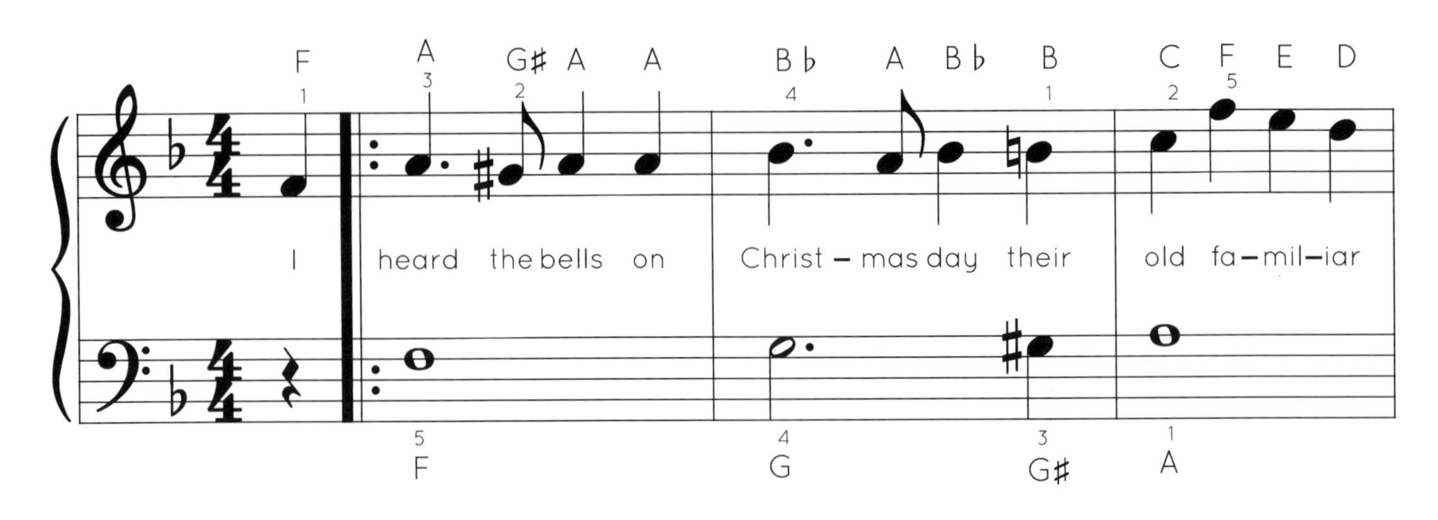

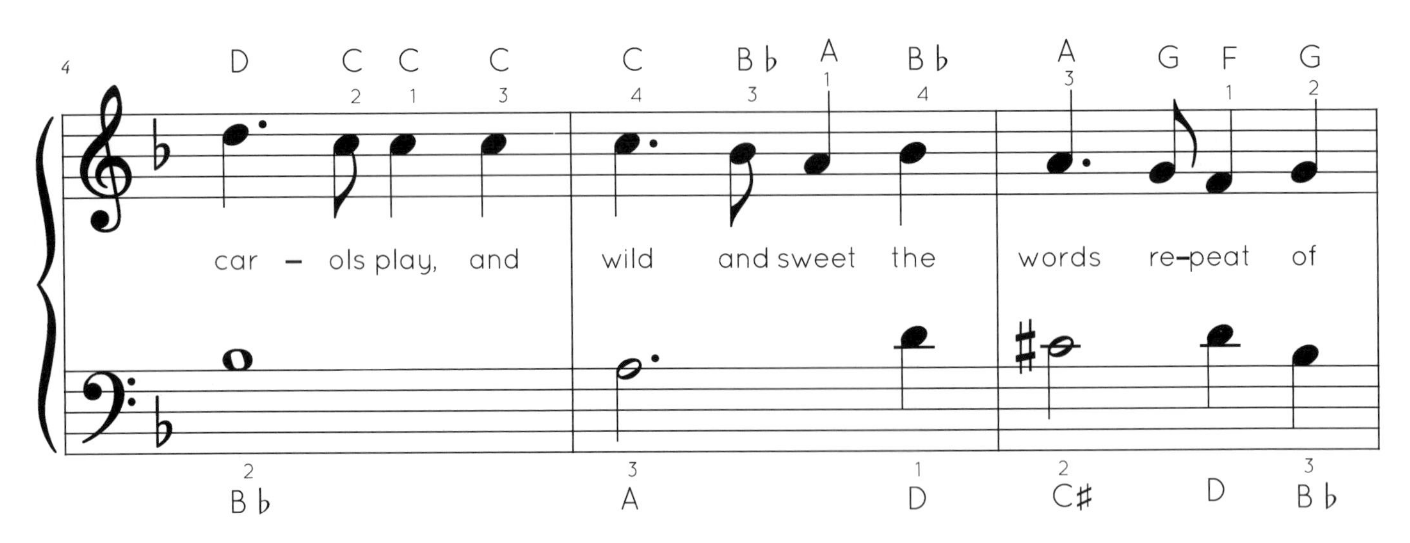

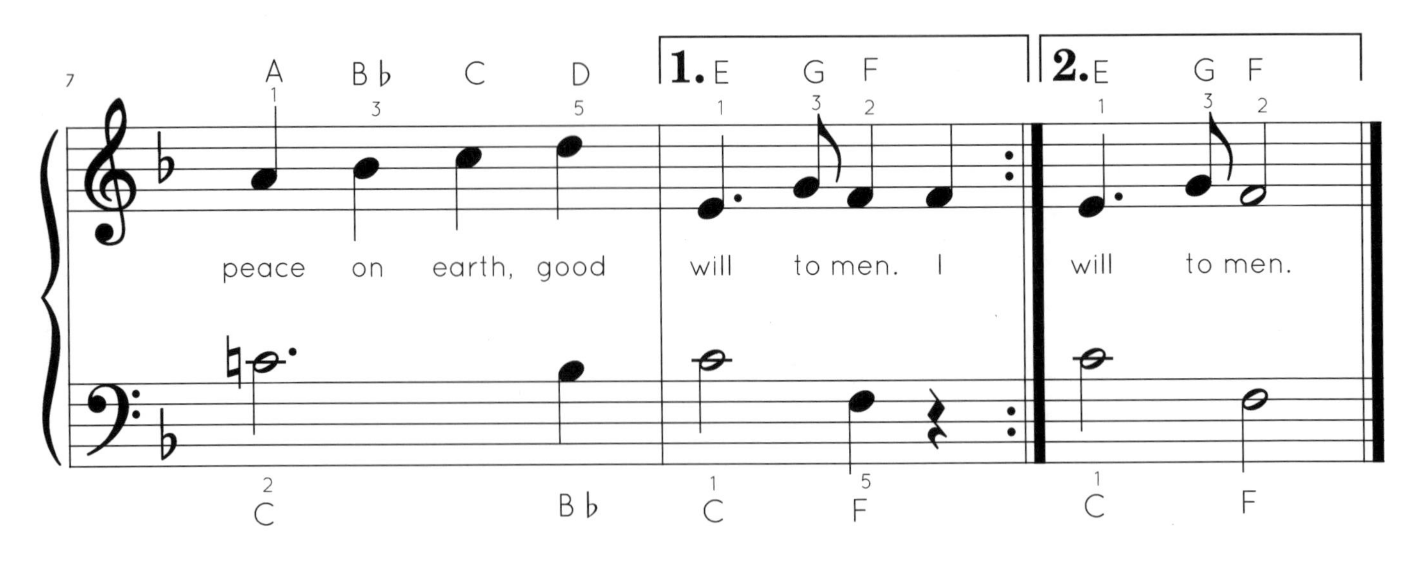

I Saw Three Ships

English folk song

The Holly and the Ivy

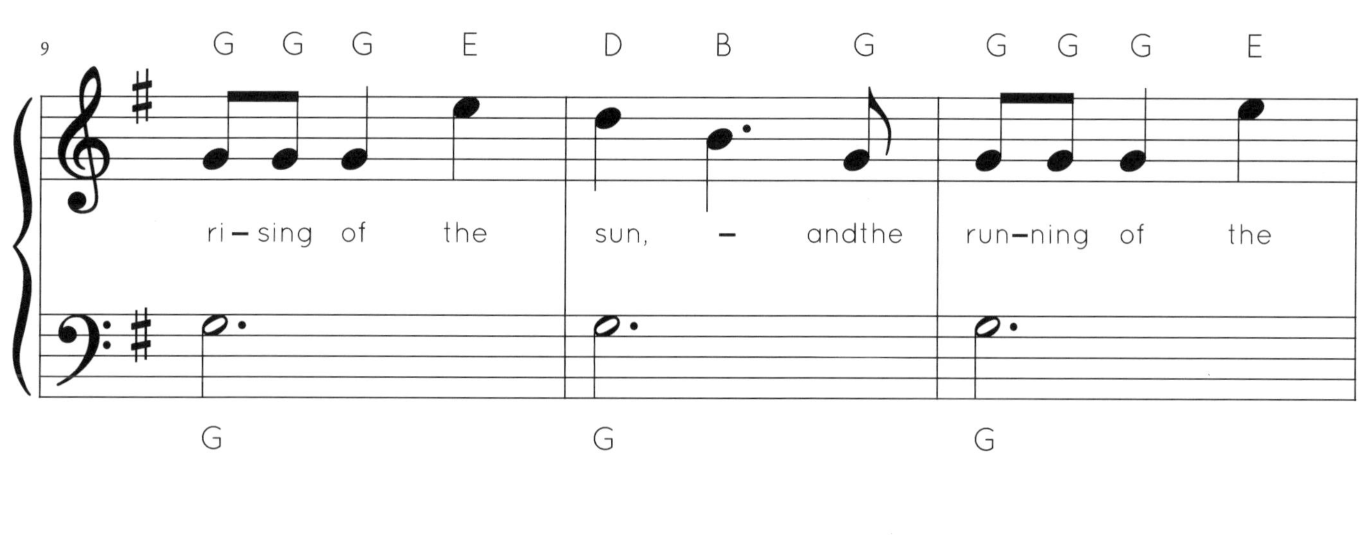
9
G G G E D B G G G G E
ri – sing of the sun, – andthe run–ning of the
G G G

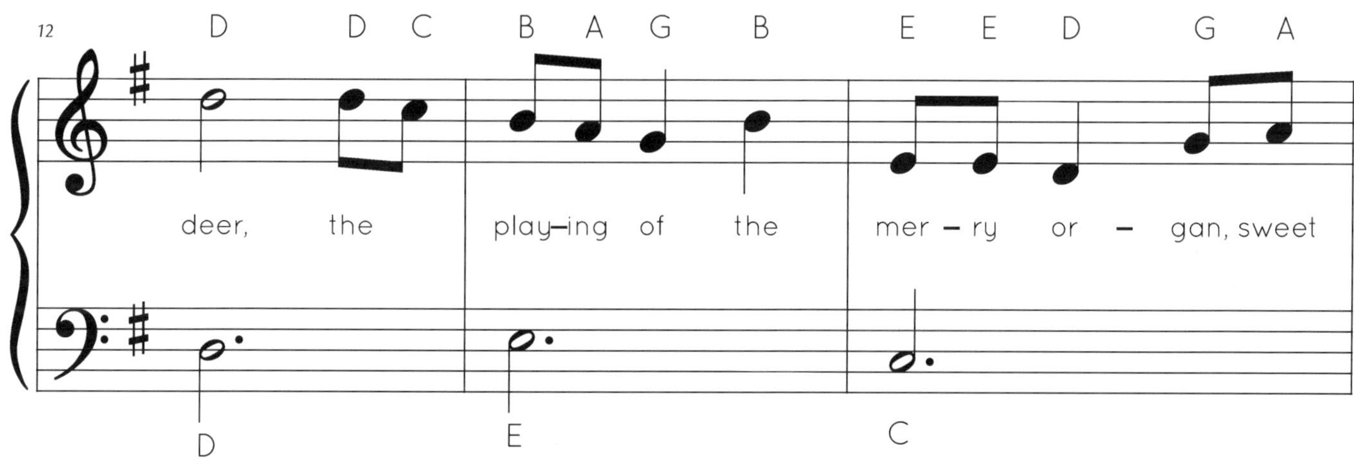
12
D D C B A G B E E D G A
deer, the play–ing of the mer – ry or – gan, sweet
D E C

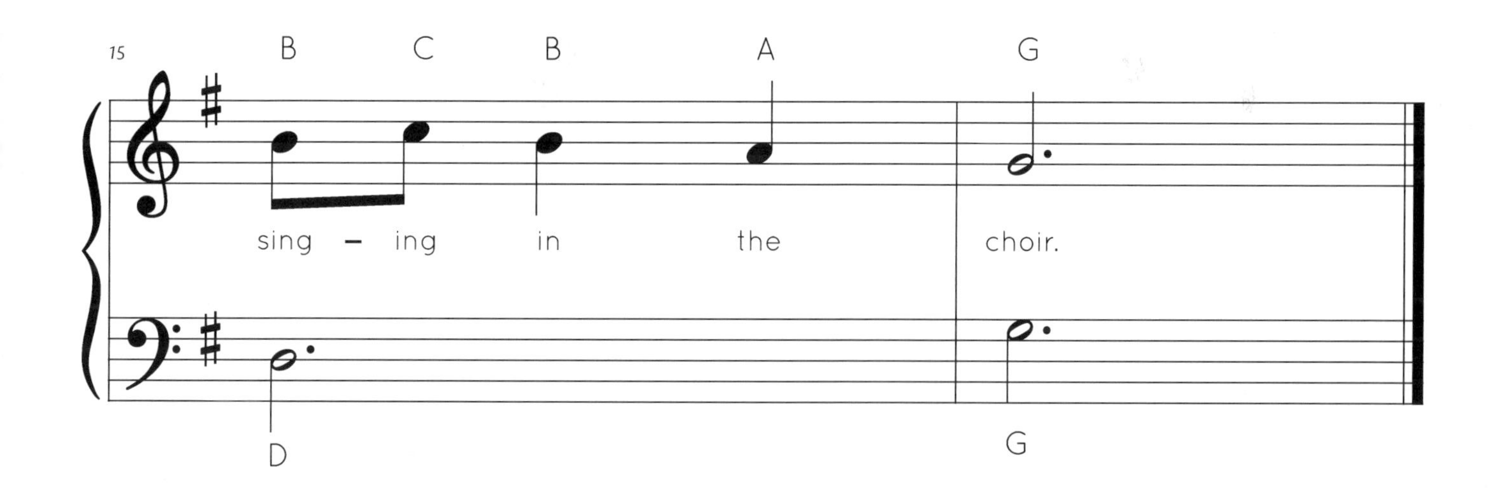
15
B C B A G
sing – ing in the choir.
D G

The Twelve Days of Christmas

Christmas carol

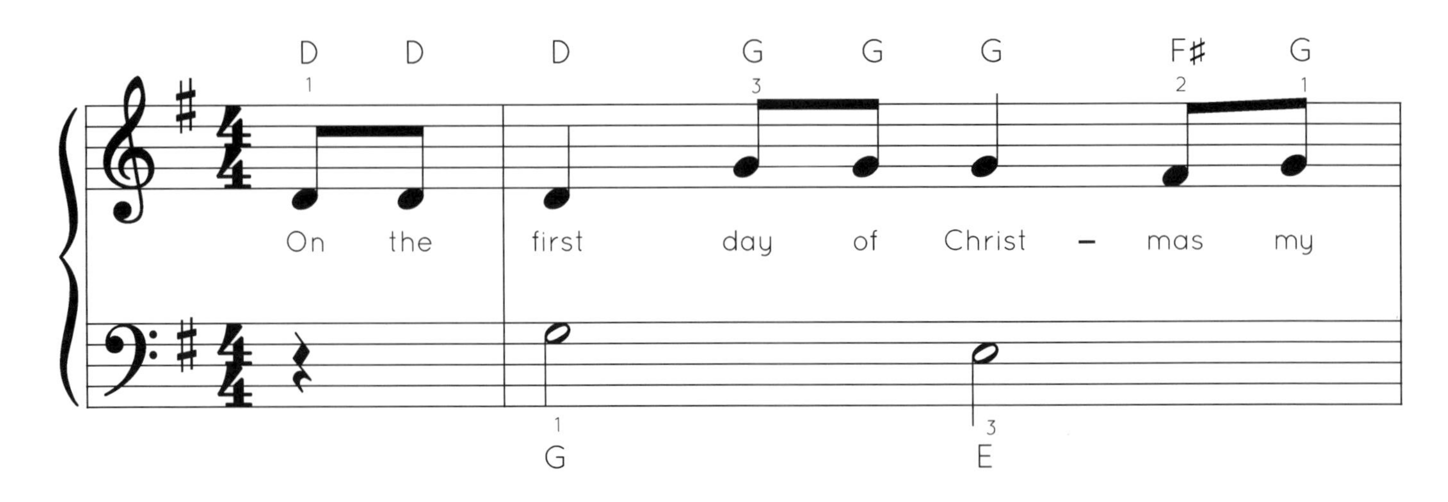

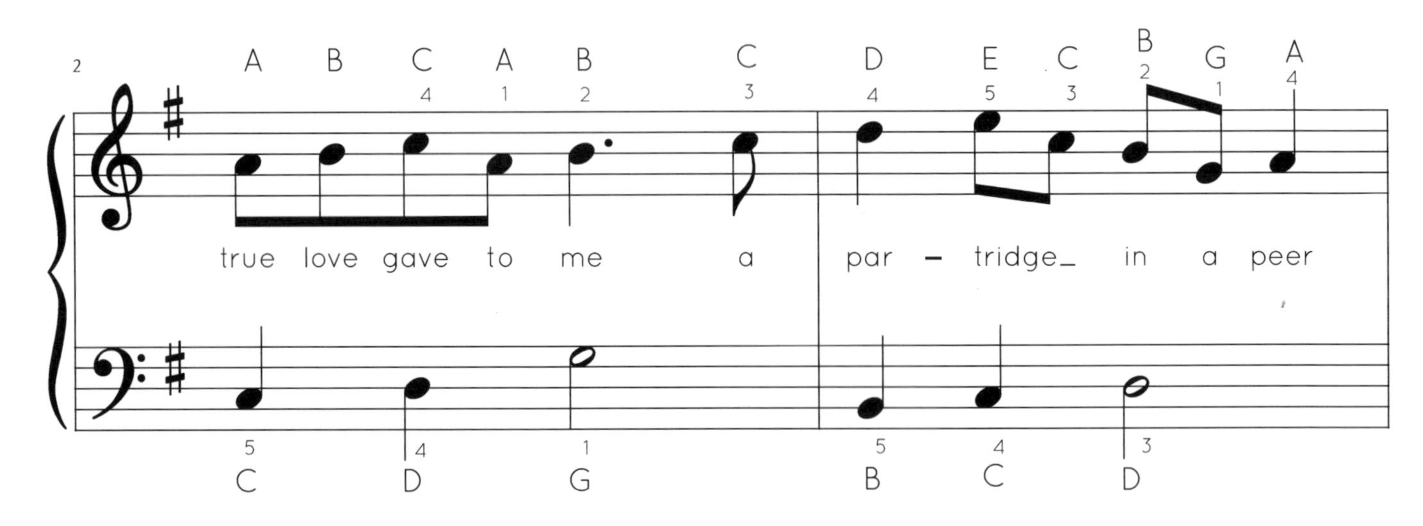

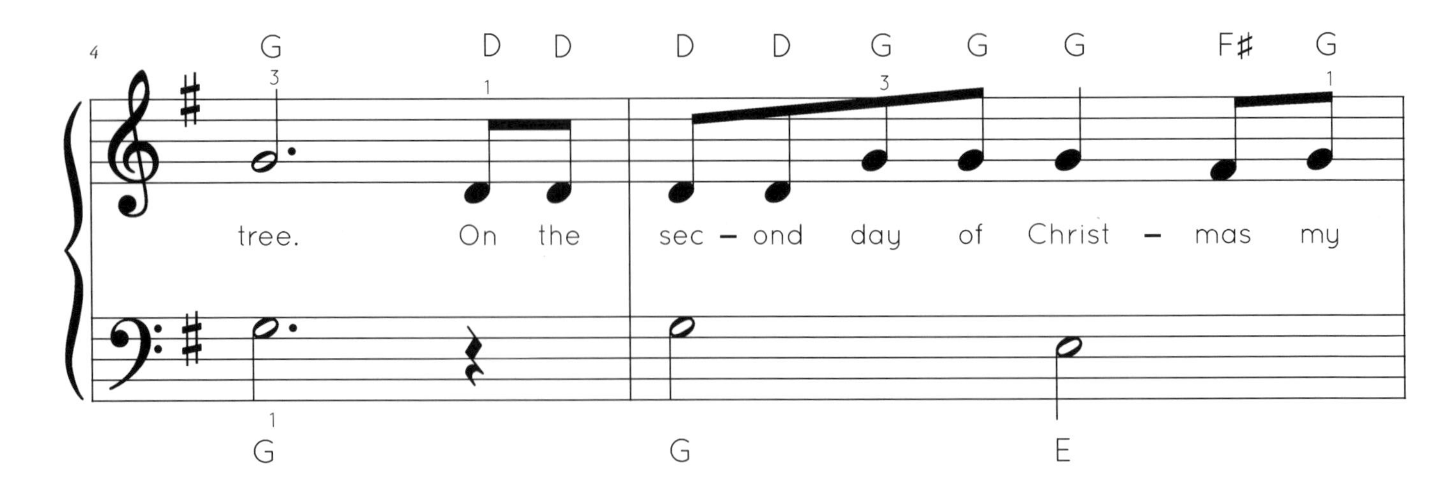

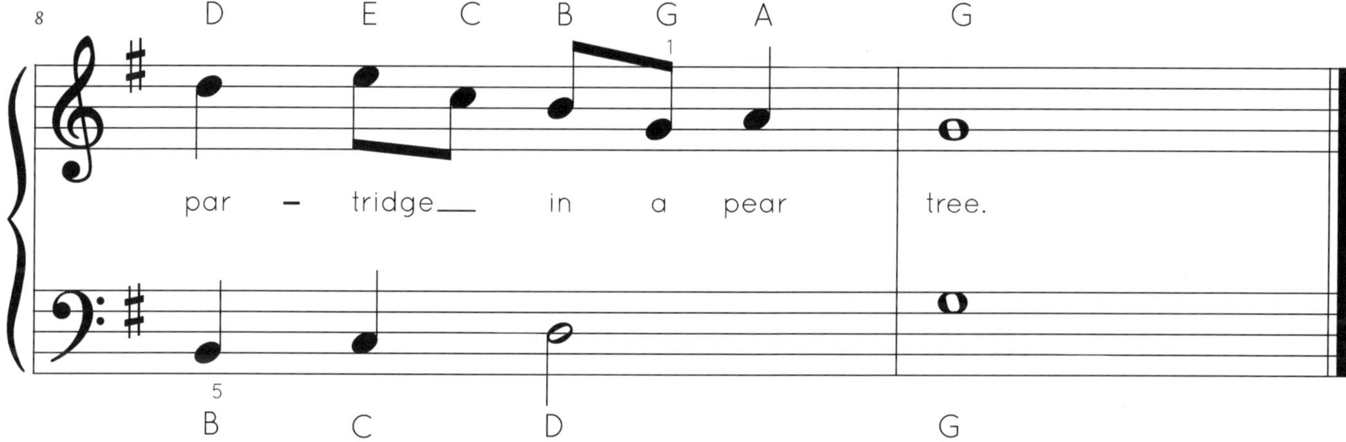

The full version of this song spans 17 pages.

To make this book (much) more afforable for you we were unable to provide the complete version of the song here due to high printing costs.

However, you can easily download the entire 17-page sheet music along with an audio file using this link: https://bit.ly/12daysofchristmas-fullversion

Alternatively, you may scan the QR code below:

We Three Kings of Orient Are

John Henry Hopkins Jr.

13
A B A G F♯ E F♯ A
Fo – lo – wing yon – der star. O
O – ver us all to reign.
Wor – ship Him, God on High.
C B E D
17
G G G D G E G
star of won – der, star of night,
G G C G
21
G G G D G E G
Star of roy – al beau – ty bright,
G G C G

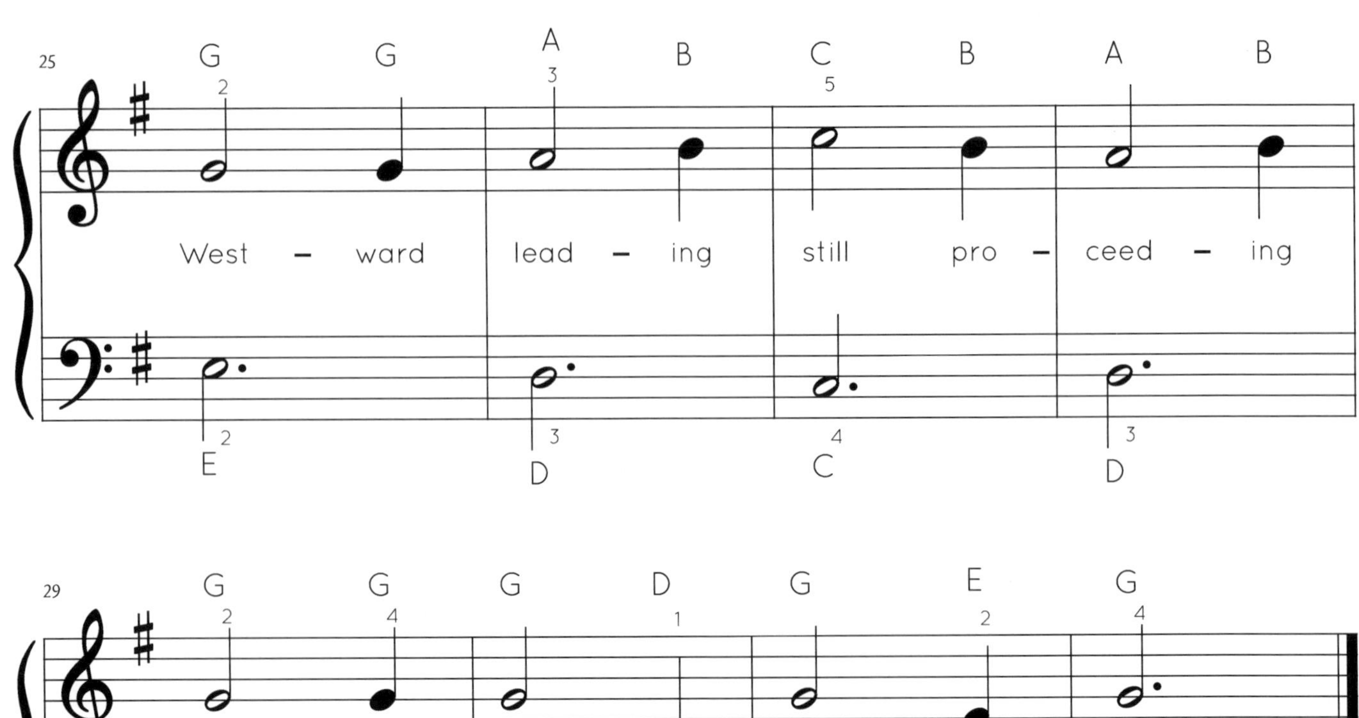

29

G G G D G E G

2 4 1 2 4

Guide us to thy per – fect light.

1 5 1

G G C G

Il est né le divin enfant

French Christmas carol

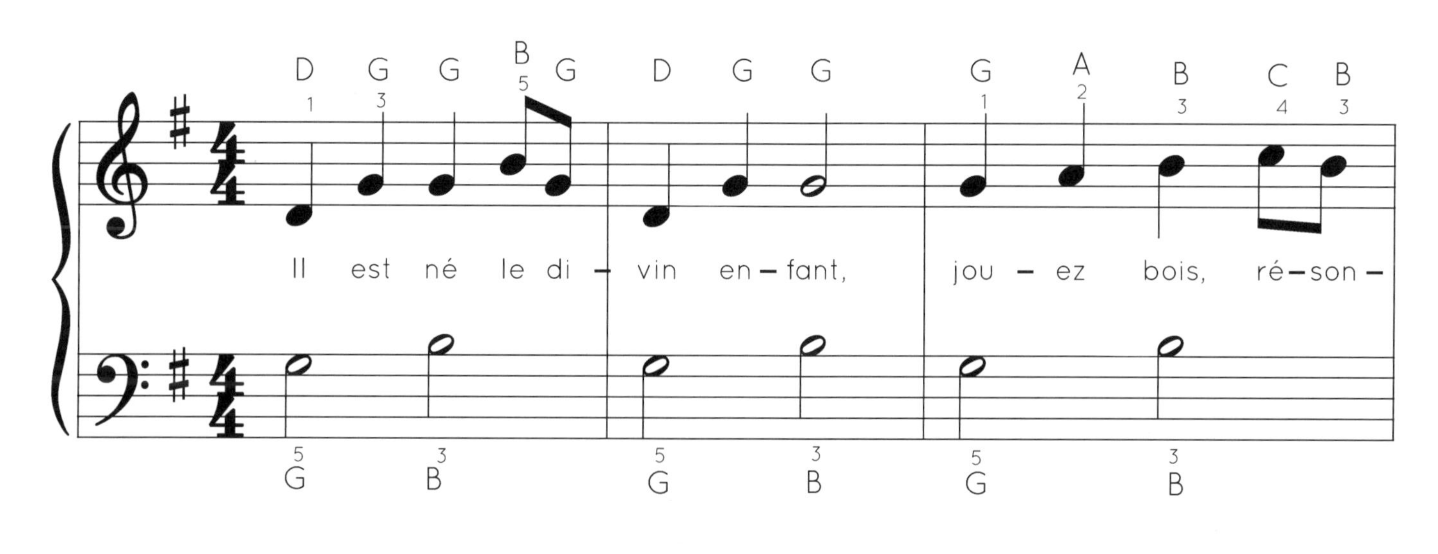

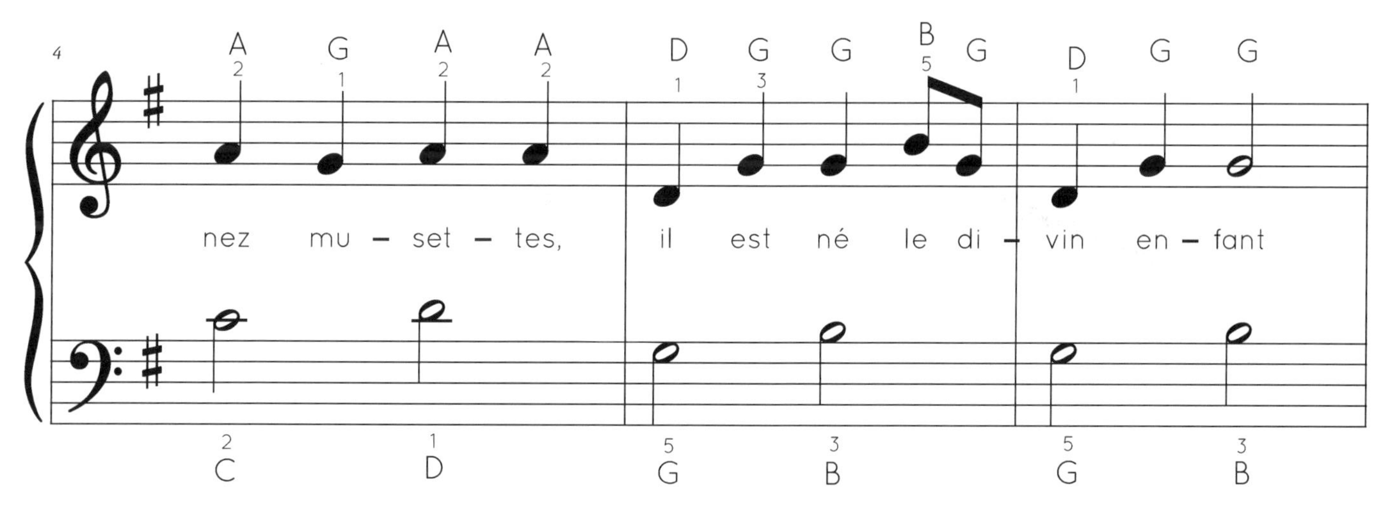

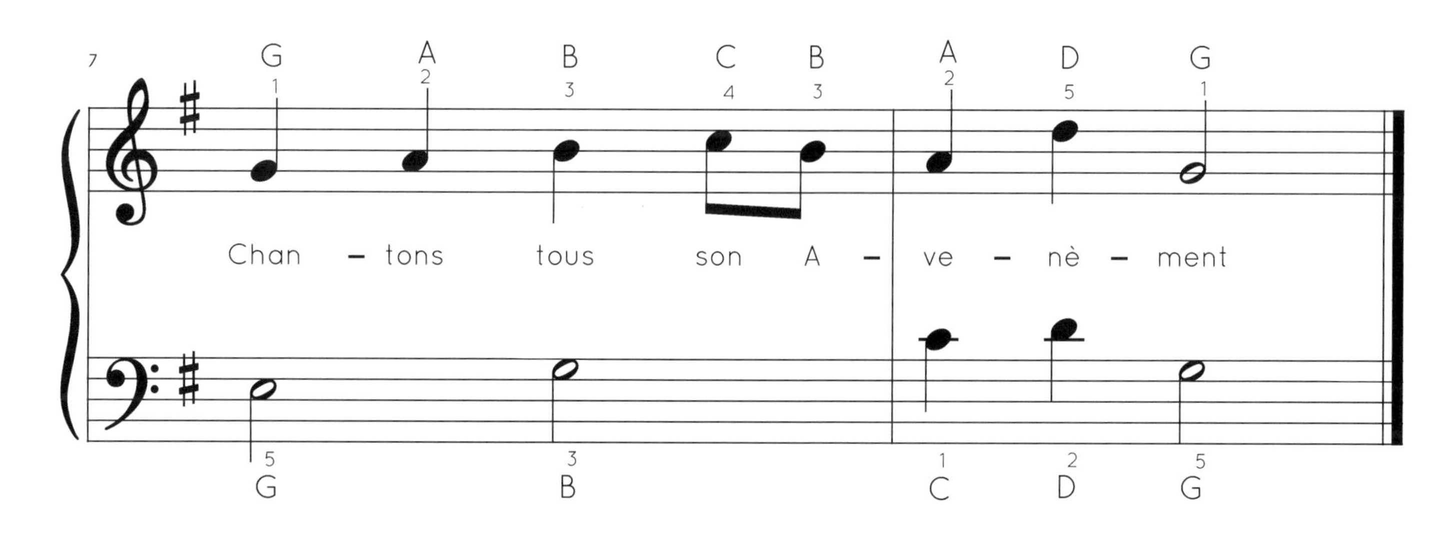

We Wish You a Merry Christmas

Christmas carol

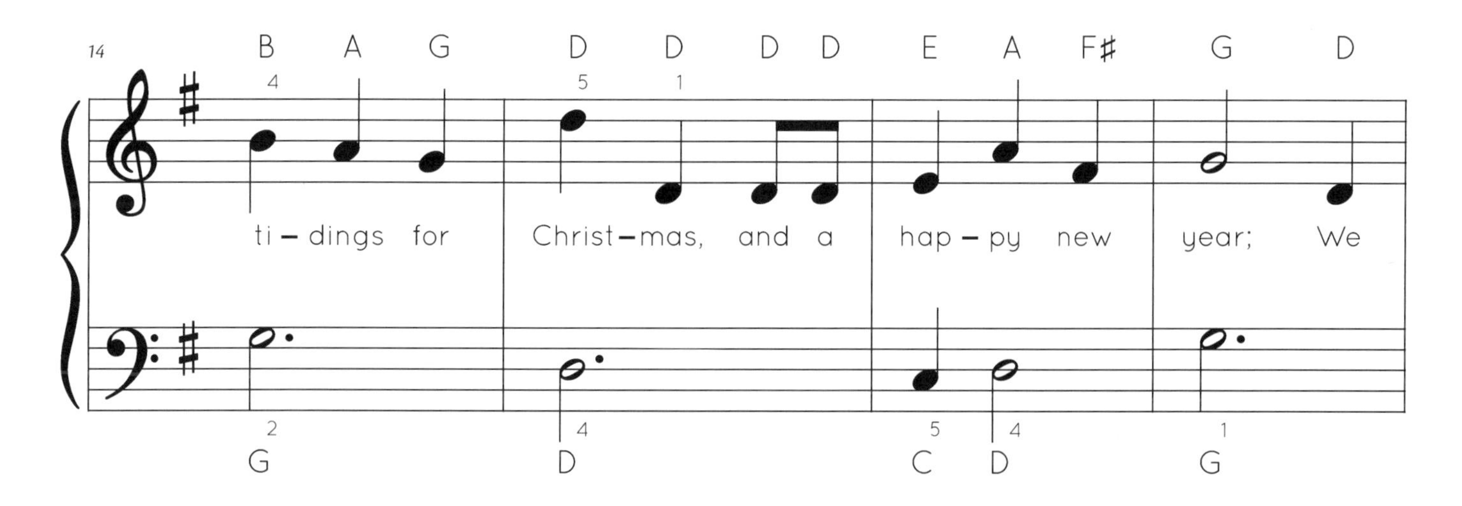
14
B A G D D D D E A F♯ G D
4 5 1
ti – dings for Christ – mas, and a hap – py new year; We
2 4 5 4 1
G D C D G

18
G G A G F♯ E E E A A B A G F♯ D D
wish you a mer–ry Christ–mas, We wish you a mer–ry Christ–mas, We
3
G C A D

22
B B C B A G E E E D A F♯ G
wish you a mer–ry Christ–mas, and a hap – py new year!
D♯ E D G

In the Bleak Midwinter

Music: Gustav Holst
Lyrcis: Christina Rossetti

C B C D E E B
snow had fal – len, snow on snow
In the bleak mid – win – ter
But his mot – her on – ly
If I were a wise man
E E C E
D B A G F♯ B B C D B
snow on snow , in the bleak mid –
sta – ble place suf – ficed The Lord God al –
in her mai – den bliss, Wor – shipped the be –
I would do my part; Yet, what can I
B C D G G
A G A B A G G
win – ter long – a – go.
migh – ty Je – sus Christ.
lov – ed with – a kiss.
give him? give – him my heart.
E E C D G

Coventry Carol

Christmas carol

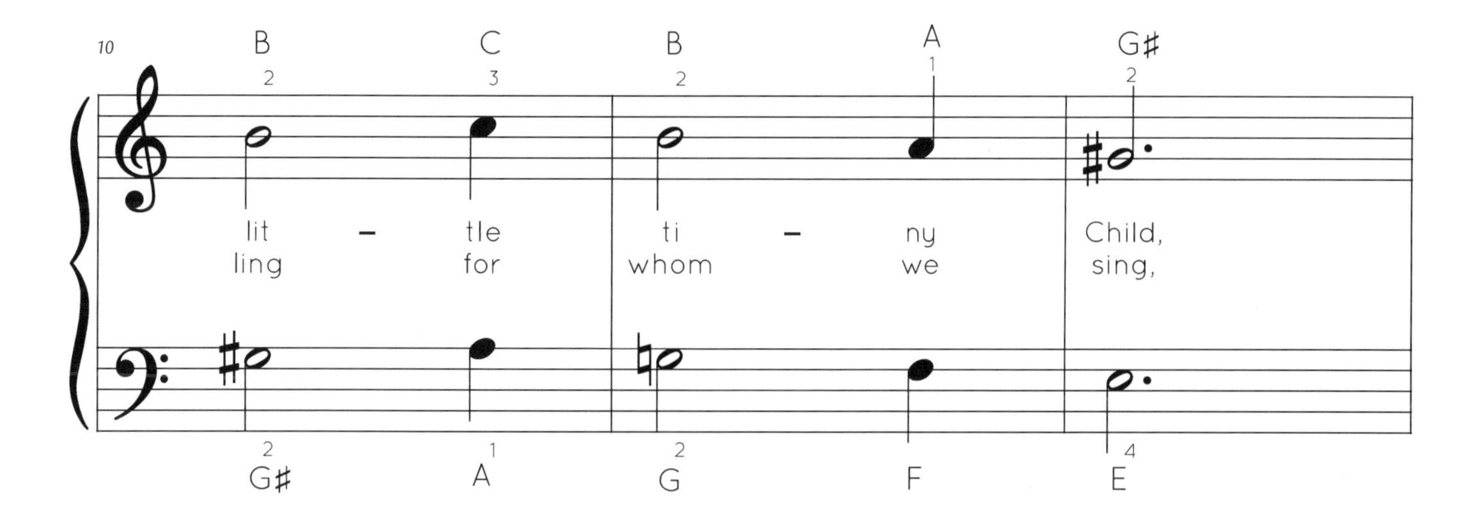
10
B C B A G♯
2 3 2 1 2
lit – tle ti – ny Child,
ling for whom we sing,
2 1 2 4
G♯ A G F E

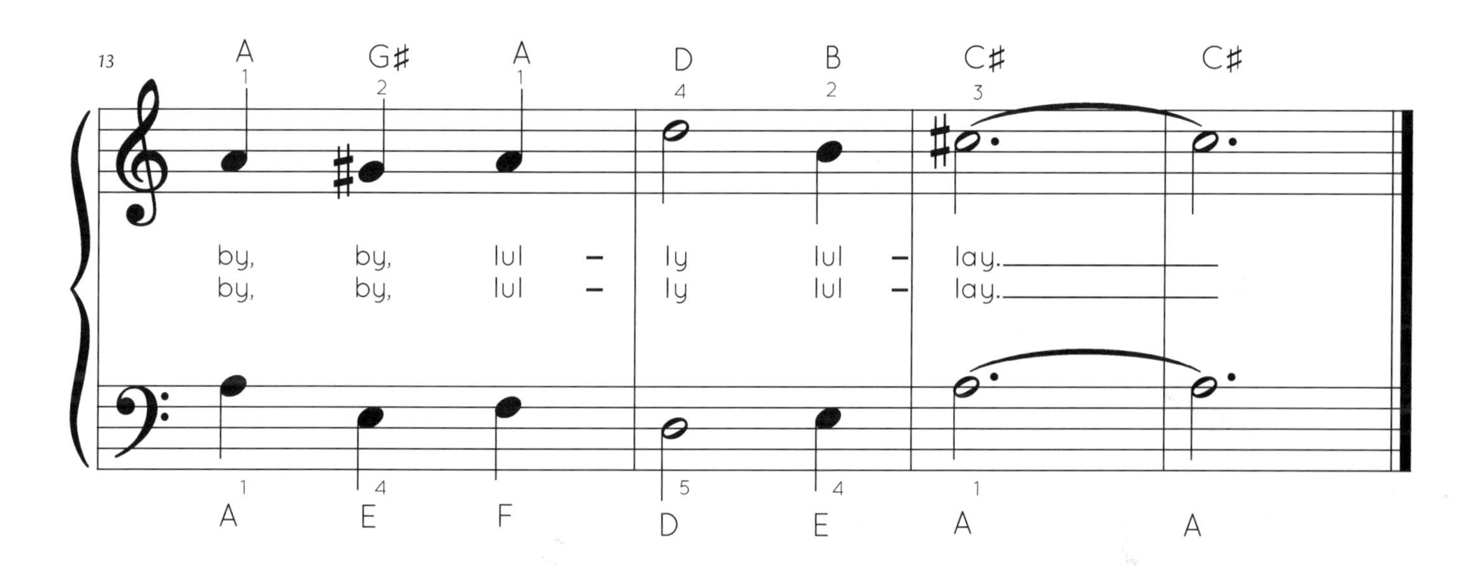
13
A G♯ A D B C♯ C♯
1 2 1 4 2 3
by, by, lul – ly lul – lay.
by, by, lul – ly lul – lay.
1 4 5 4 1
A E F D E A A

What Child is This?

Melody: English folk song
Lyrics: William Chatterton Dix

Lasst uns froh und munter sein

German Christmas carol

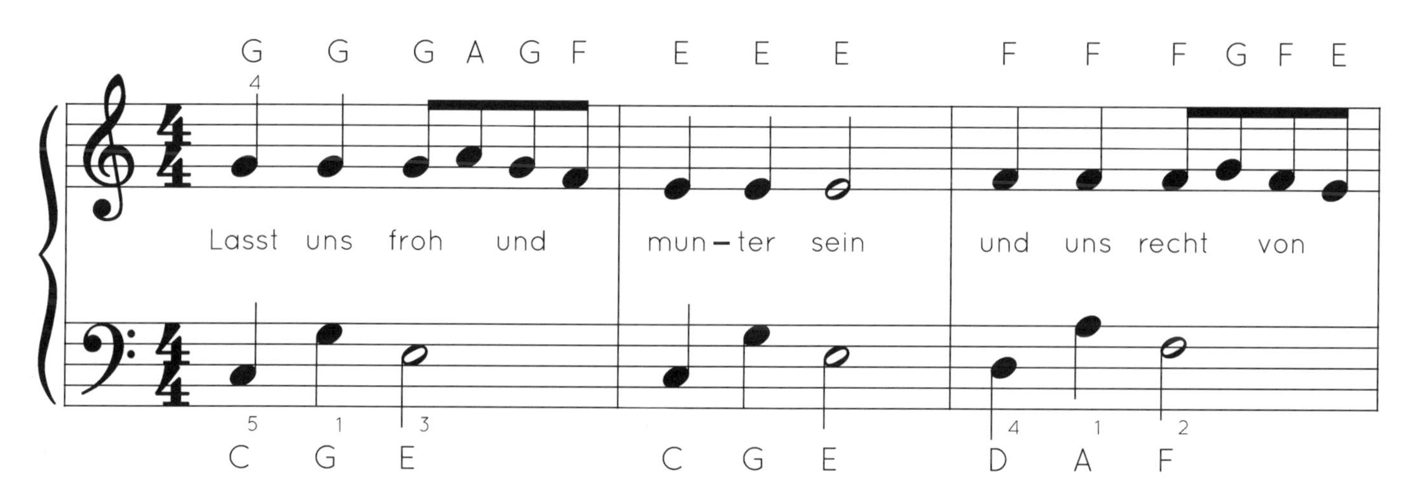

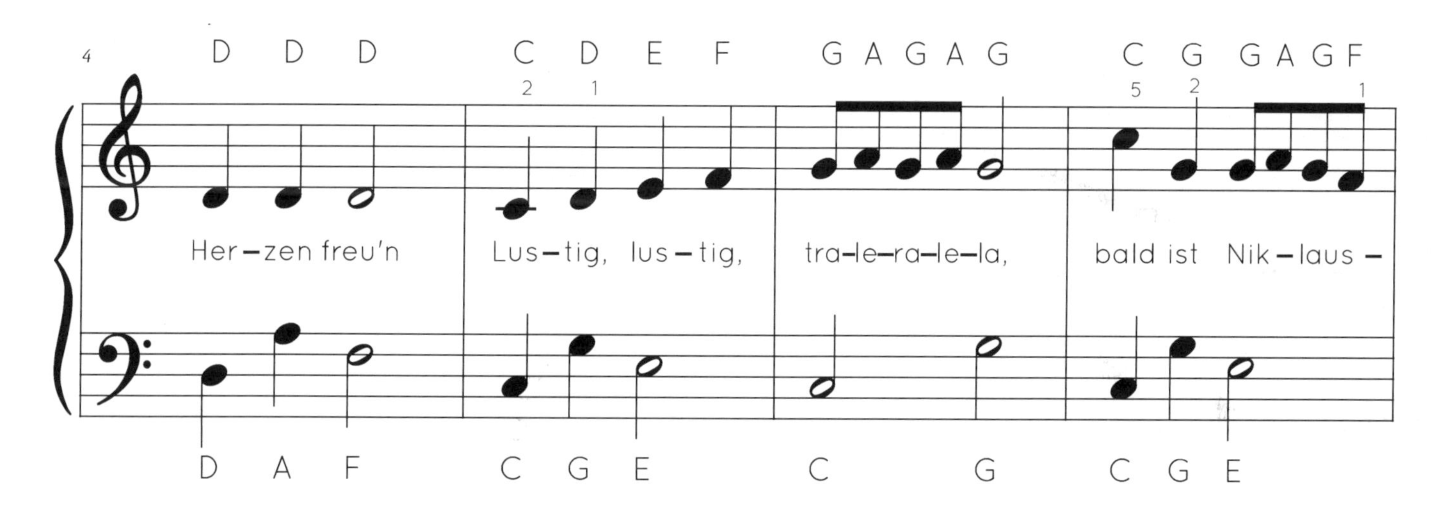

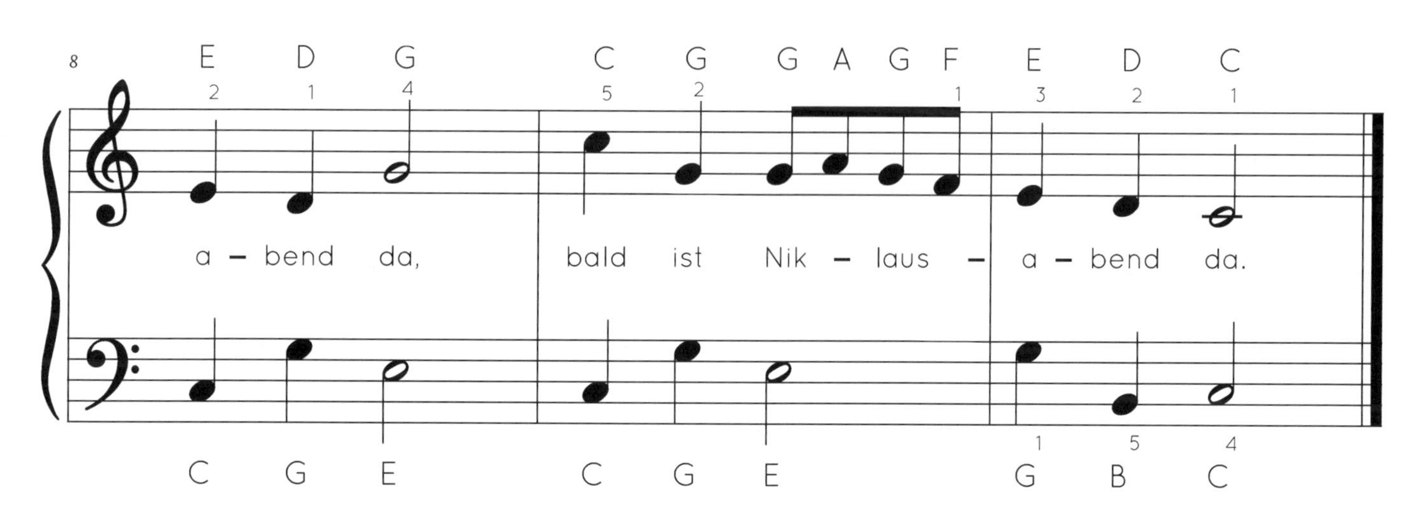

Auld Lang Syne

Music: Scottish folk song
Lyrics: Robert Burns

10
C A A F G F G D C A A C
4 2 2 1 2 1 2 5 4 2 4
auld lang syne, my jo, for auld lang
3 5 1 2 1
A F C C D D C
13
D D C A A F G F G A G
5 4 2 1 3 2 3
syne, we'll tak' a cup o' kind – ness yet, for
3 1 2 5 4
B♭ A F C C
16
F D D C F
2 1 2 1 3
auld lang syne.
5 3 2 1
B♭ D E F

Good King Wenceslas

Christmas carol

9
D C B A B A G
Bright – ly shone the moon that night,
"Sire, he lives a good league hence,
Page and mon – arch, forth they went,
B A G F♯ G F♯ E
11
E D E F♯ G G D D E F♯
though the frost was cru – el; When a poor man
un – der – neath the moun – tain, right a – gainst the
forth they went to – ge – ther trough the rude wind's
C B C D G G B B C D
14
G G A D C B A G C G
came in sight, gath–'ring win – ter fu___ el.
for – est fence, by Saint Ag – nes foun___ tain.
wild la – ment and the bit – ter wea___ ther.
E E F♯ D C B A G F♯ E C G

The Wexford Carol

Irish Christmas carol

9
C C C C C B♭ G F D E♭ F E♭ G F
1 1 4 3 2 1 2 3 2 4
lo – ved – son. With Ma – ry ho – ly we should pray to –
in the town. But mark how all things come to pass: From
in great fear. "Pre – pare and go" the an – gels said, To
1 2
C B♭ B♭
12
E♭ D C C G A B♭ C B♭ G C C B C D
2 1 2 3 1 3 4
3
God-with love – this Christ–mas day; In Beth – le – hem up
ev – 'ry door re – pelled a – las! As long – fore – told, they
Beth le – hem, be not a – fraid; For there you'll find, this
4 1
C G C
15
E F G E F G E C D C C C
on that morn There was a bless–ed Mes – se – ah born.
ref – uge all, Was but a hum – ble ox – 's stall.
hap – py morn, A price – ly babe. Sweet Je–sus born.
4 1
B A G C

O du fröhliche

German Christmas carol

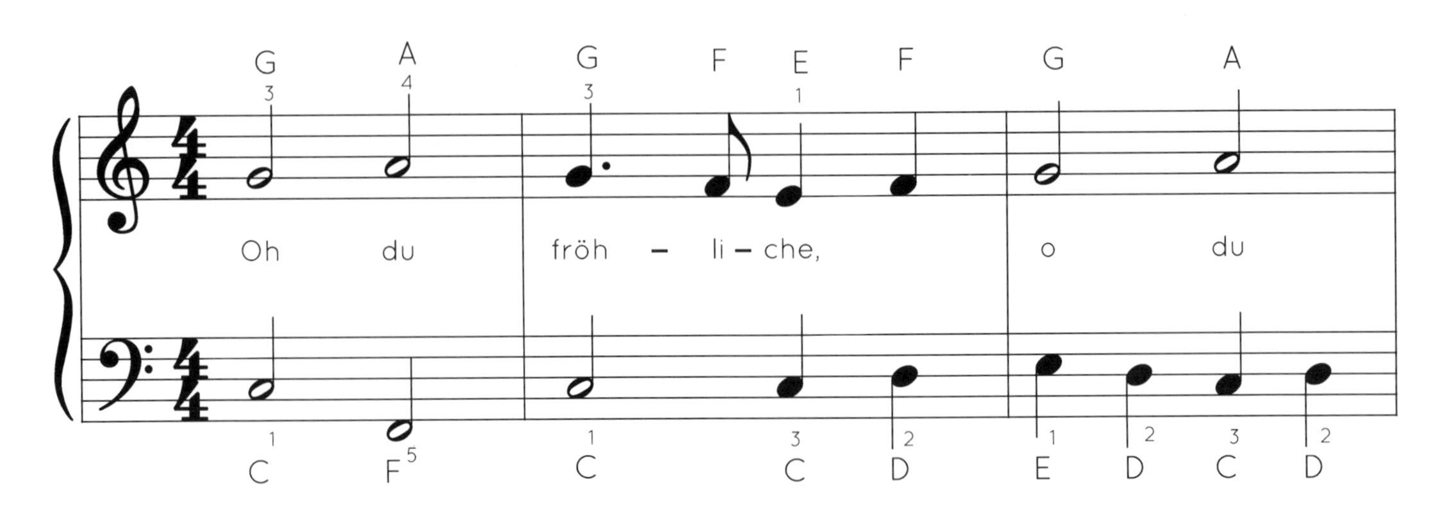

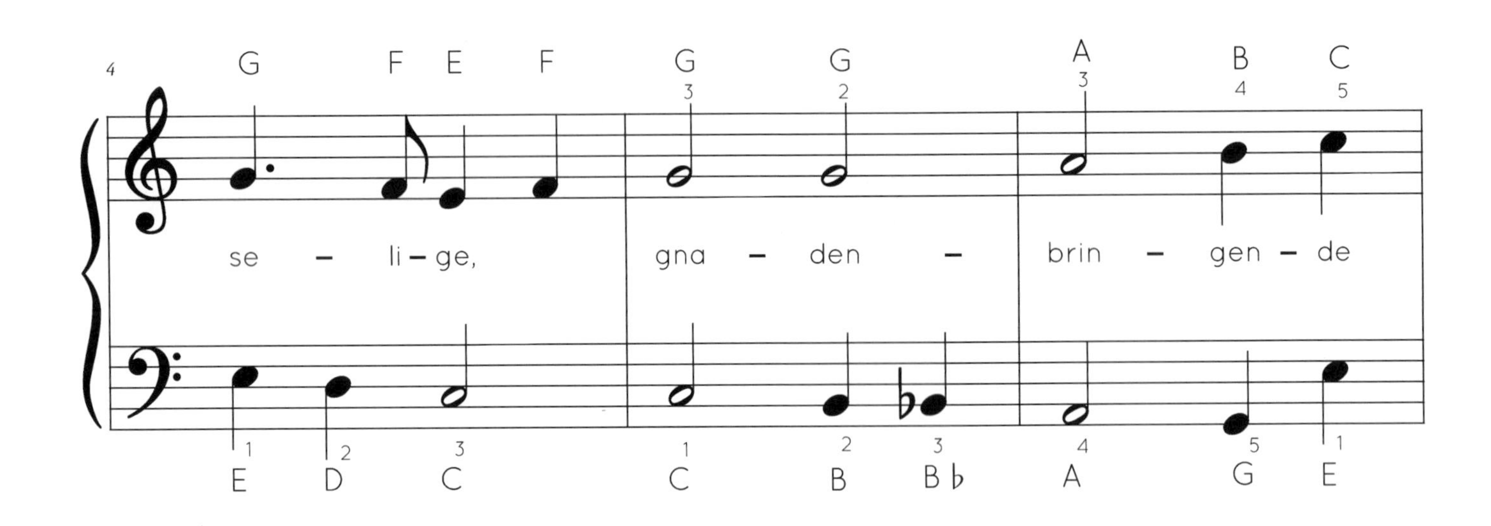

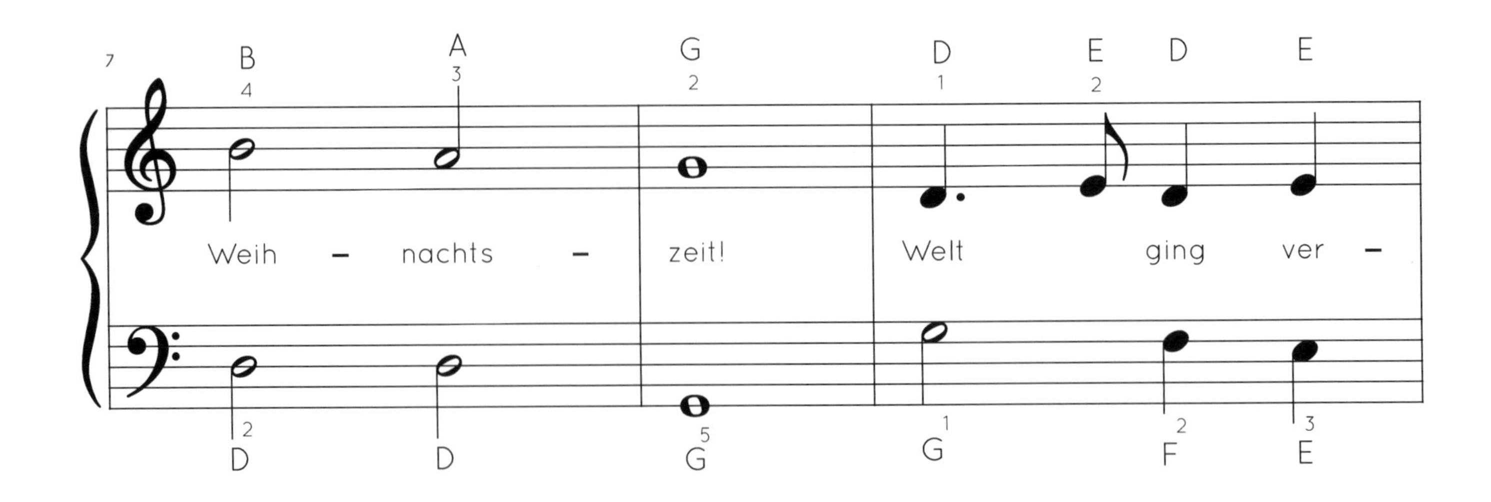

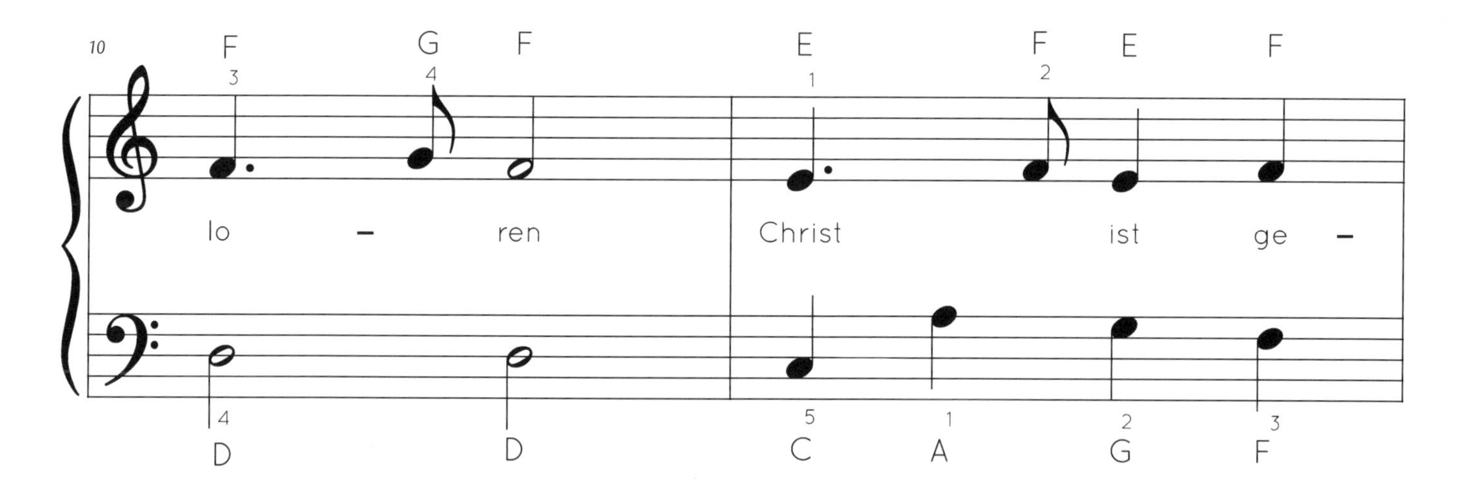
10
F G F E F E F
3 4 1 2
lo – ren Christ ist ge –
4 5 1 2 3
D D C A G F

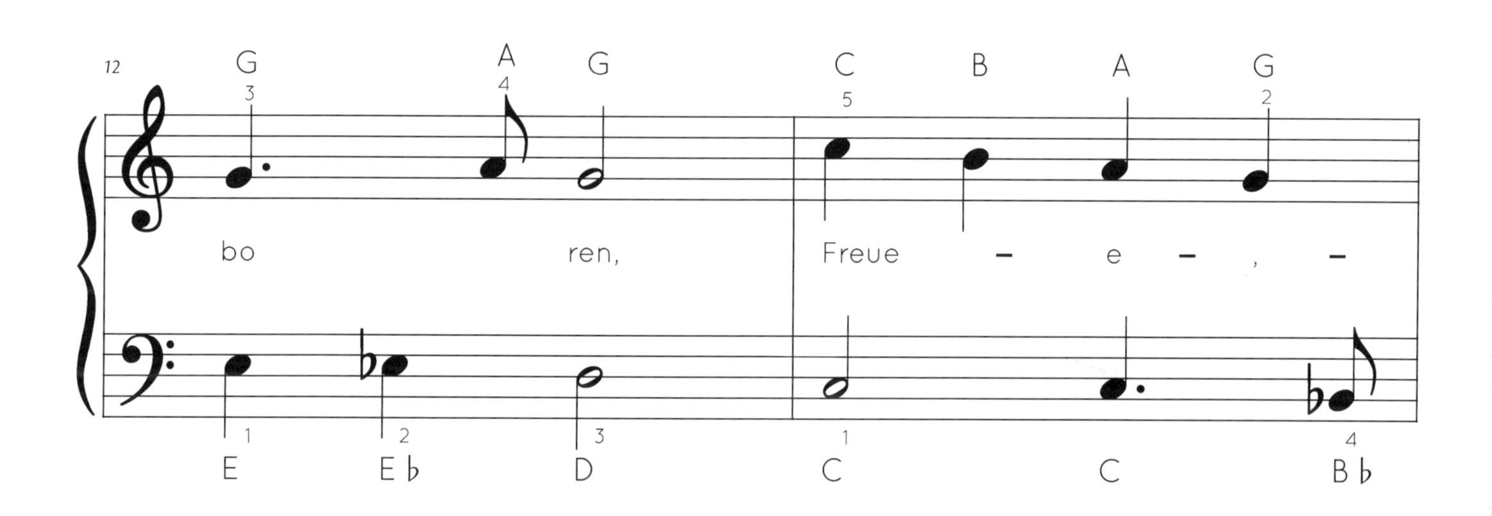
12
G A G C B A G
3 4 5 2
bo ren, Freue – e – , –
1 2 3 1 4
E E♭ D C C B♭

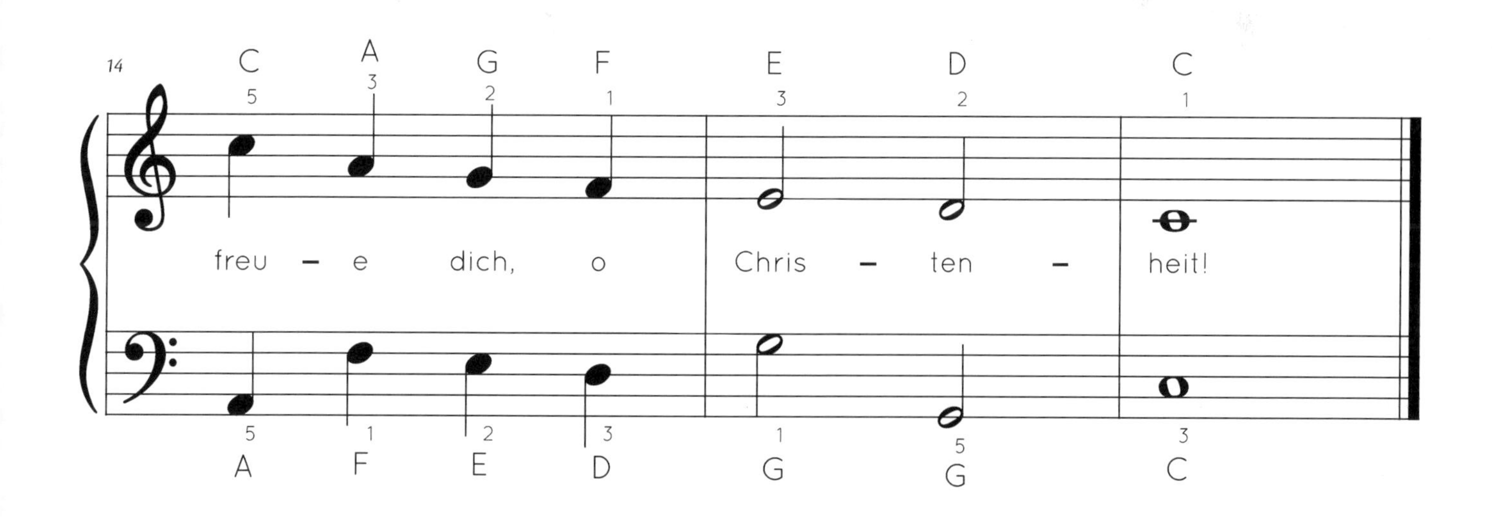
14
C A G F E D C
5 3 2 1 3 2 1
freu – e dich, o Chris – ten – heit!
5 1 2 3 1 5 3
A F E D G G C

Dejlig er jorden

Norwegian Christmas Song

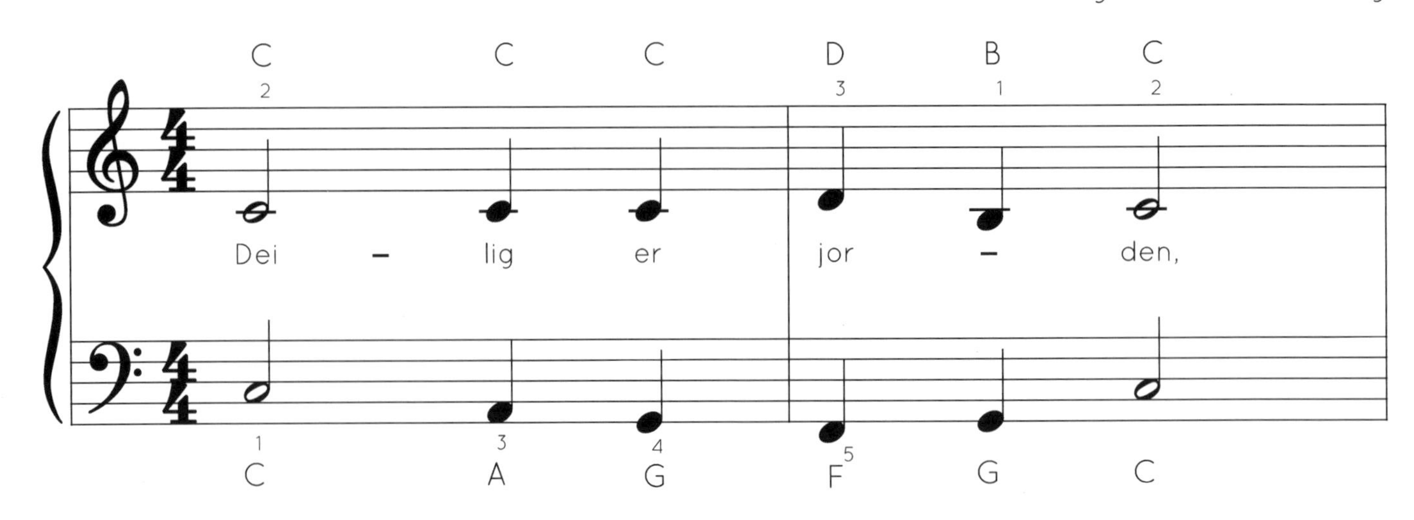

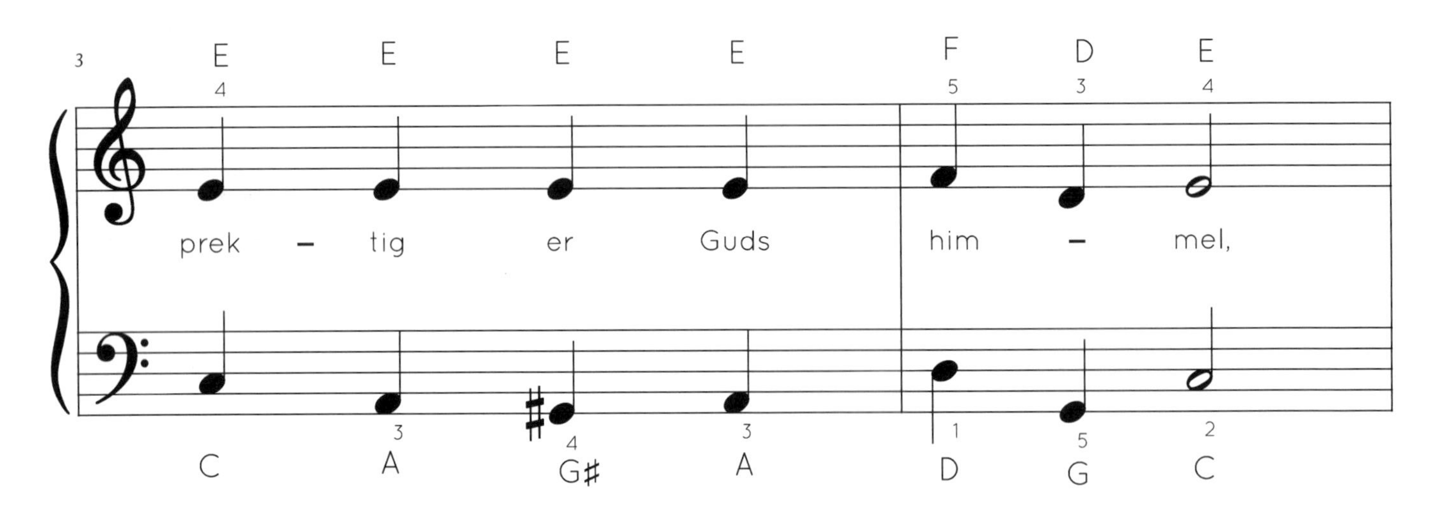

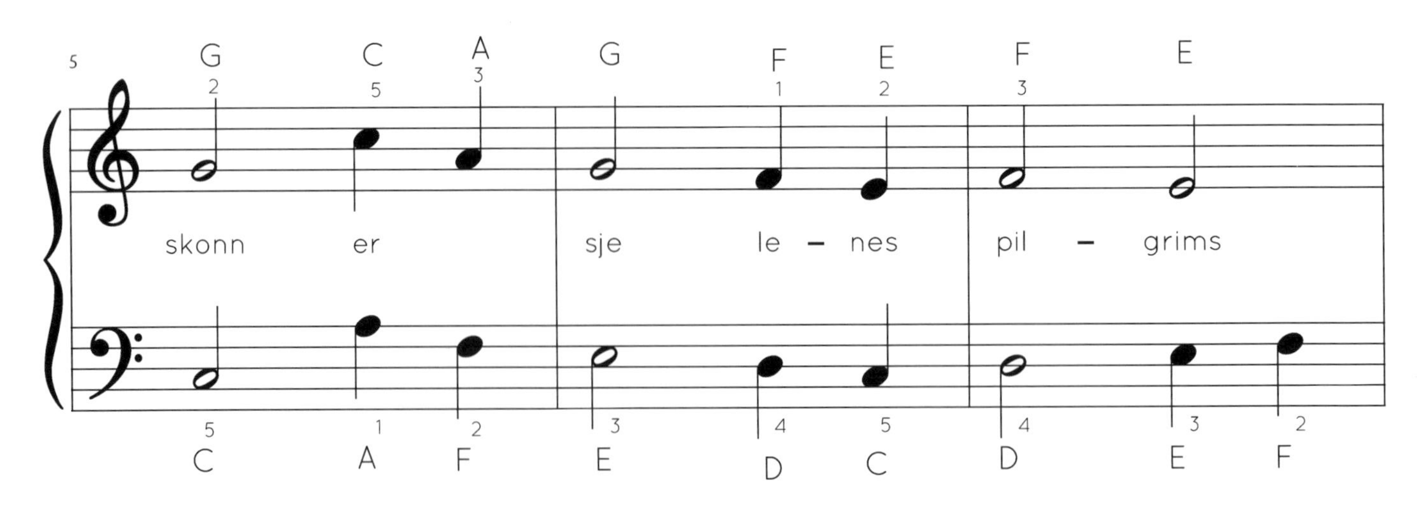

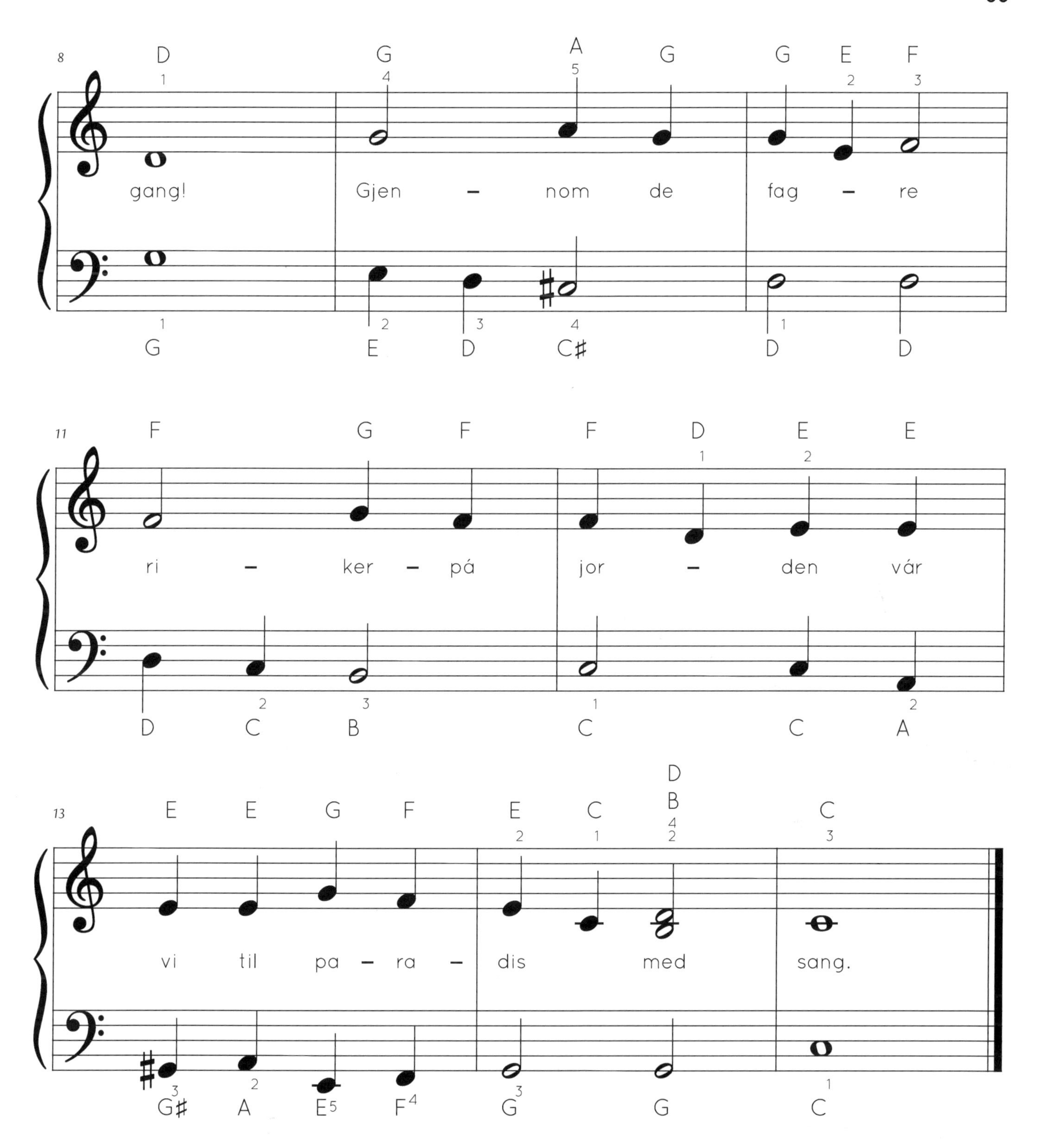
8
D G A G G E F
1 4 5 2 3
gang! Gjen – nom de fag – re
1 2 3 4 1
G E D C♯ D D
11
F G F F D E E
1 2
ri – ker – på jor – den vår
2 3 1 2
D C B C C A
13
E E G F E C D B C
2 1 4 2 3
vi til pa – ra – dis med sang.
3 2 5 4 3 1
G♯ A E F G G C

Jingle Bells

Music and lyrics: James Lord Pierpont

12
E E E C B A D D D D
bright, What fun it is to ride and sing a
lot; he got in – to a drift – ed bank and
speed, then hitch him to an o – pen sleigh and
G C A C A F♯
15
E D C A G B B B B B B
sleigh – ing song to – night! Jing – le bells, jing – le bells,
we, we got up – sot!
crack! you'll take the lead!
C F♯ B G D B G B F♯
19
B D G A B C C C C
jing – le all the way! Oh what fun it
B G C A D G E C E C

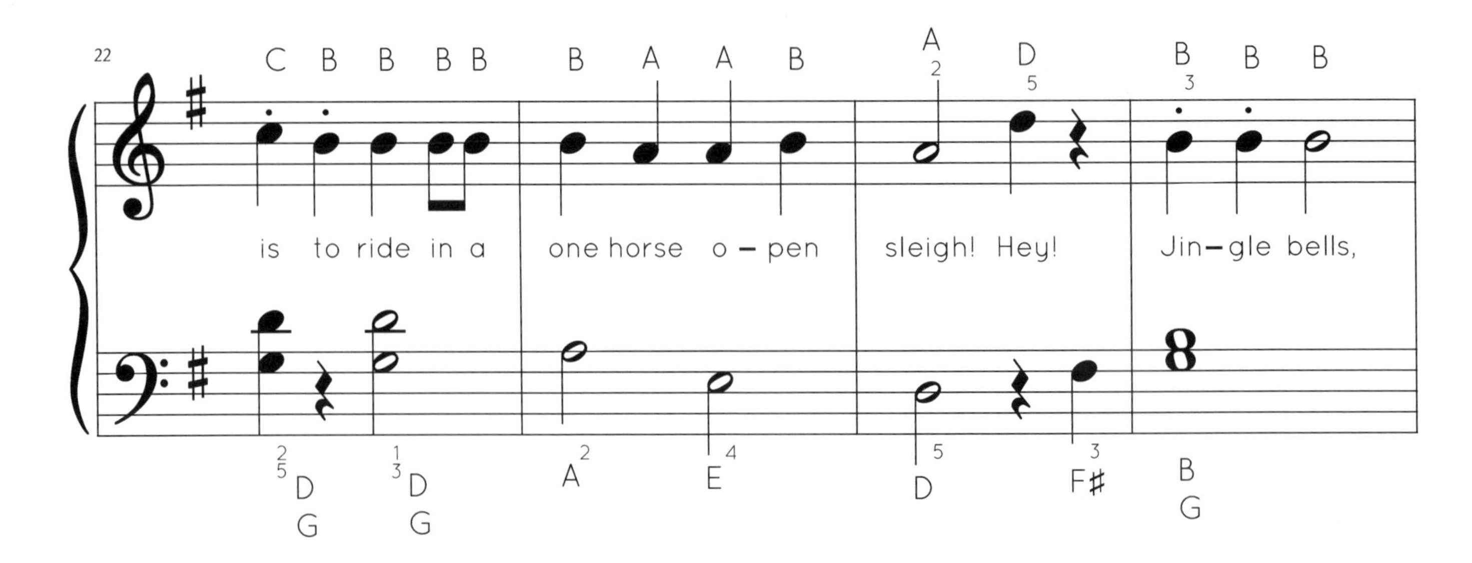
22
C B B B B
B A A B
A
2
D
5
B
3
B B
is to ride in a
one horse o – pen
sleigh! Hey!
Jin – gle bells,
2
5
D
G
1
3
D
G
2
A
4
E
5
D
3
F♯
B
G

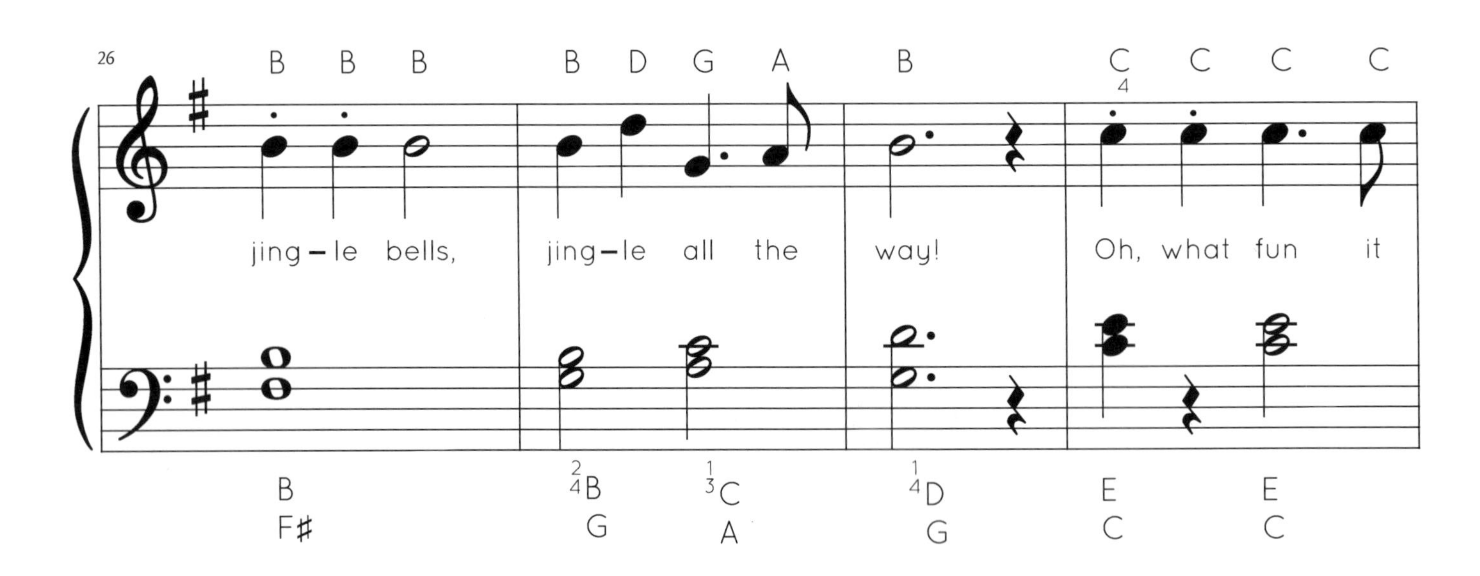
26
B B B
B D G A
B
C
4
C C C
jing – le bells,
jing – le all the
way!
Oh, what fun it
B
F♯
2
4
B
G
1
3
C
A
1
4
D
G
E
C
E
C

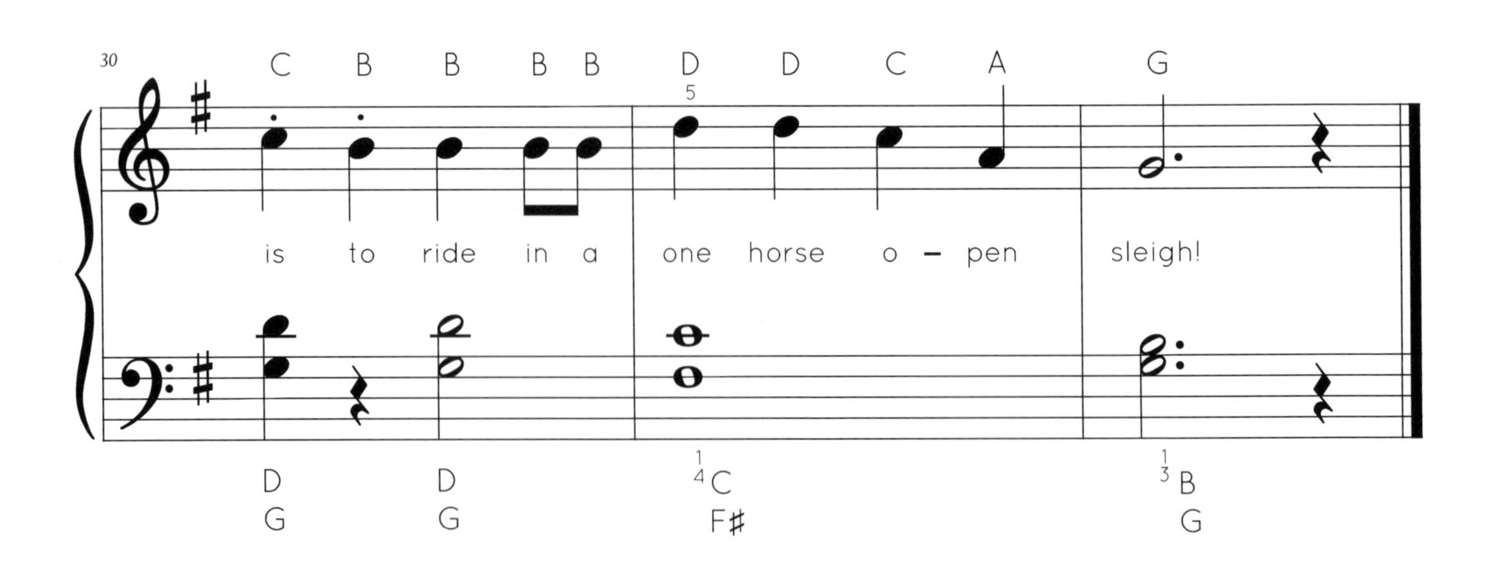
30
C B B B B
D
5
D C A
G
is to ride in a
one horse o – pen
sleigh!
D
G
D
G
1
4
C
F♯
1
3
B
G

Go Tell It on the Mountain

Christmas carol

D E D B B G A A G A
kept their watch – ing, O'er si – lent flocks by
feared and trem – bled When lo! A – bove the
low – ly man – ger Our hum – ble Christ was
G G G D D
B G B D D E D B
night Be – hold through – out the hea – vens –
earth, Rang – out the an – gel cho – rus
born, And god sent us sal – va – tion,
G G G G
B G A A G E D C B
– There shone a ho – ly light. Go,
That hailed our Sav – ior's birth:
That bles – sed Christ – mas morn:
G D E D D G

33
B A G E D G A A A G A
5 4 3 1 2 5 2
tell it on the moun – tain, o – ver the hills and
G G G D D
4
38
B D E D B B A G E D G C
e – very where Go, tell it on the moun – tain that
G D G G G G
44
B B A G A G
Je – sus Christ – is born.
D D G

Free Audio Files from the Book

This book also includes access to free audio recordings in mp3 format to help you learn and practice. The songs were recorded by a professional pianist playing accurately and slowly each song on a piano so you know exactly what it should sound like.

HOW TO DOWNLOAD THE AUDIO FILES?

To download the audio files, go to the following link or scan the QR code:

https://bit.ly/christmas-carols-for-piano

On the website, please enter your name and your email. Then, click "DOWNLOAD".

Go to the inbox of the email you have just entered. Find the email sent from "Sontig Press" with the subject "Please Confirm Your Subscription". If you cannot find the email, please also check your Spam or Promotions folders.

Once you have confirmed your email by clicking the button "CONFIRM YOUR EMAIL", you will receive a new email with the subject "Here are your audio files!". Clicking the link in the email (or the image) will give you an instant access to the audio recordings of the songs from the book!

You can download each file separately or all files at once (0. All audio files.zip).

Thank you for buying this book. If you are enjoying it, we'd like to ask you to **leave a review for it on Amazon**. It takes less than a minute.

Also, join our Facebook Group to get more free piano learning material (including free or discounted piano books, when they are published).

Do you have any questions or remarks about the book? If so, then send us an email at info@sontigpress.com and we'll be happy to help you.

Other Books by the Publisher

Primo Piano. Easy Piano Music for Adults. 55 Timeless Piano Songs for Adult Beginners with Downloadable Audio by Aria Altmann

In this book, you will find 55 musical pieces for (advanced) beginners. The book features well-known world classical pieces, famous English evergreens, and international folk songs.

Little Pianist. Piano Songbook for Kids: Beginner Piano Sheet Music for Children with 55 Songs (+ Free Audio) by Aria Altmann

This book includes 55 very simple and easy songs for absolute beginners. All songs include fingerings and the easiest songs also include key letters. The book features well-known children's songs and nursery rhymes, simplified classical pieces, as well as famous English evergreens and international folk songs.

Classical Piano Masterpieces. Piano Sheet Music Book with 65 Pieces of Classical Music for Intermediate Players (+ Free Audio) by Christina Levante

In this book, you will find 65 splendid pieces of classical music for intermediate players. The book features well-known world classical pieces as well as some beautiful less-known classics which often don't get enough recognition.

Made in United States
Troutdale, OR
11/09/2023